A GUIDED TOUR THROUGH SPACE AND TIME

Eva Fenyo

A GUIDED TOUR THROUGH SPACE AND TIME

Prentice-Hall, Inc.
Englewood Cliffs, N. J.

TO THE MEMORY OF
MY MOTHER AND FATHER

Library of Congress Catalog Card Number 59-10919

Printed in the United States of America

37090

FOREWORD

The idea for this book was conceived in 1945 during the Russian siege of Budapest. As the weeks of incessant bombardment dragged on, the fear which we of our apartment building had experienced was gradually replaced by just plain hunger and monotony. Huddled together in the small bomb shelter in the basement, we had nothing to remedy the first but beans and dried peas. To relieve the second, however, each of us in turn suggested games to play. When my turn came, I would present mathematical puzzles or problems from the realm of physics. That bomb shelter, in fact, was the birthplace of my spacetime explorer with his special equipment and unlimited imaginative power.

Shortly after the end of World War II, his exploits resulted in a short book. It was received so well that my publishers wished me to expand it to cover the complete story of theoretical physics. Just as this task was begun, however, I was suddenly arrested for "political reasons" by the Communist secret police. I was "tried," together with my mother and my husband, and sentenced to a long prison term at forced labor.

Each day I worked at constructing a factory. Occasionally our team of women prisoners would manage to exceed our "work quota" and, for this, small rewards were granted. All I personally wanted, was a pencil, some paper, and permission to write.

"Science is a very good thing," declared the prison Commandant, a former farm-hand who had retained some good healthy common sense under his layer of Communist indoctrination. "Your request is granted—on one condition. You must write this book so that I myself shall be able to understand every word of it."

Thus I became perhaps the only political prisoner in Hungary to possess a pencil and a copybook. Writing whenever I was permitted to do so, I tried to keep in mind what the Commandant had told me. In a way, I was writing the book for him—which meant for all laymen. He never saw the completed manuscript, though, for I was suddenly transferred to another prison camp.

When I was finally released, I found that all my books had been banned by the Communist censors. Conditions grew increasingly intolerable in Budapest, and my husband and I decided to risk an unusual escape from the Iron Curtain country which our beloved Hungary had become. One night two large packing cases, ostensibly loaded with heavy furniture, were shipped toward the Austrian frontier. Hardly daring to breathe, my husband occupied one of them and I the other. My manuscript was the only possession I had taken with me.

The escape was successful. After a nerve-wracking twenty hours of confinement, we crawled out with stiff backs—*but we were free!*

From Europe we managed to get to America, where the writing of books one believes in is not forbidden. In completing this one, I have not forgotten my promise to the prison Commandant. I have tried to present pure physics in such a way that anyone—even if he has no previous scientific training—can clearly grasp it.

The author is indebted to Dr. Robert T. Beyer, Professor of Physics at Brown University, for his patience in reading the manuscript and for his helpful suggestions. Special thanks are also due Mr. David C. Knight of Prentice-Hall, without whose editorial help the manuscript might never have reached publishable form. In addition, I should like to thank Mr. Peter Costanza who transformed the author's own drawings into finished products, and Mrs. Louise Grather for her cheerful and competent typing of the manuscript.

EVA FENYO

CONTENTS

CHAPTER △ ONE

SCIENCE-FICTION OR SCIENCE-FACT?

THE "PANCAKE EFFECT"

PROSPECTUS OF THE GUIDED TOUR

OUR SPECIAL EQUIPMENT

To begin our guided tour through space and time, let us look briefly into the distant future and examine two items appearing in the plastic pages of the *New York Herald-Times* of April 7, 2159.

The first is an engagement announcement:

> Mr. and Mrs. Harley King of Flushing announced yesterday the engagement of their daughter Janice, age 15, to Lt. John Farnsworth, recently discharged from the United Nations Lunar Service where he held the post of Communication's Officer at Kepler City.
>
> The couple has set their nuptial date for June 17, 2161, at which time the bride shall have reached the legal marriageable age of 18. Mr. Farnsworth, now 26, has placed himself in the hands of Time Adjustment Bureau officials, as is customary in such matches. A TA booking agent said yesterday that Mr. Farnsworth would take the Earth-to-Alpha Centauri Flight leaving Idlewild next week. The Lightship is scheduled to return to Earth in three years, whereupon Mr. Farnsworth shall have aged but five weeks while his bride shall have reached her 18th birthday.

The second item bears an interplanetary dateline. Its syndication by the Solsystem News Service indicates that it appears in all daily papers serving colonies of Earthmen on Mars and the Moon. Accompanying the item is a photograph of a man inside the transparent cabin of a spaceship. The man looks very strange indeed. The picture shows him looking as if he had been flattened by a huge rolling pin.

This item reads as follows:

> Space research teams, operating some 20,000 miles beyond the orbit of Pluto, released this exclusive Teleradarfoto yesterday, showing the effect on a human body of velocities nearing that of light.
>
> Successfully employing ultra-fast colloidal lenses, technicians were able to obtain photographic proof of the "pancake effect," or the contracting of a man's body as it speeds through space at 100,000 miles per second. This phenomenon was predicted as early as the beginning of the 20th century by Einstein's equations.
>
> U.N. space research scientists declined to reveal the name of the crewman for security reasons.

In the first item, young Lt. Farnsworth, who is not as young as he would like to be, has fallen in love with an extremely young girl and cannot marry her for three years. By the time his fiancée is old enough, Lt. Farnsworth feels, there will be too great an age differential between them. The lieutenant, however, lives in an age where it is possible to absent himself temporarily from the Earth's time system. Time Adjustment Bureau arranges a "three-year" trip for him, during which he will participate in an entirely different time system from that of his fiancée. Upon his return he will have aged only a few weeks; he will still be twenty-six while his bride-to-be has become eighteen.

In the second story we actually see, in the person of the anonymous space crewman, what will happen to Lt. Farnsworth. The crewman shrank; time contracted for him; his clocks slowed down; and biological aging itself was reduced in proportion to the extent that time for him was distorted by ultra-fast motion.

Now, being a logical person, perhaps you will object that these stories are nothing but pure fiction. You are right, they are. Yet, they *could* be true under certain circumstances. What are these circumstances and what can the layman learn about them? Can a person who is not a trained physicist ever hope to comprehend the spectacular achievements of our Atomic Age and the theories which lie behind them?

We believe that he can. It is, in fact, the aim of our Guided Tour to clarify some of these problems.

Perhaps the main obstacle in understanding these theories—many of which have changed the age-old beliefs of classical science—is that they do not, generally speaking, concern themselves with everyday experience. Nevertheless, we are going to attempt to explain them in everyday terms.

Consider, therefore, that the drawings provided in this book are actually snapshots, which we, as tourists, shall be taking on our Guided Tour. We shall also be making our own experiments in Relativity and other subjects by means of comparison and illustration. If, at times, these seem fantastic, remember that we have especially tailored them to give maximum understanding of our subject. Do not be surprised therefore when mention is made of transparent spaceships traveling at the speed of light, of elevators in outer space, or of asteroids suddenly landing on railroad tracks.

As a matter of fact, to be able to perform these experiments at all we shall have to assume that we are in possession of scientific equipment better than that available in any modern laboratory. With it, we shall be able to see as far as we wish, to make measurements from distances of several thousand miles, and to move about inside the atom as easily as we would in our own living rooms.

The accompanying illustration (Fig. 1) shows the equipment we will need for the Guided Tour. Although this device may resemble a spacesuit, it is actually far more efficient. Serving one of our eyes, for example, is a perfect telescope enabling us to see distinctly the faintest star of the remotest galaxy. For the other eye there is an electron-microscope so sensitive that it can pick up the smallest particle in nature for our examination. For audio equipment we have super-sensitive microphones, and our hands and arms will have at their disposal the most accurate of clocks, yardsticks, spectroscopes and protractors. These instruments will be capable of computing for us with equal precision the distances which separate the planets as well as those which divide one electromagnetic wave from its neighbor. Again, one "leg" of the suit will enable us to flash through space with nearly the speed of light, while the other will allow us to achieve such complete immobility as could never actually exist in nature for the sake of certain experiments. A camera, a

Geiger counter and a set of delicate scales complete our equipment.

During our Guided Tour we shall see that the science of measurement, which is nothing more than a comparison of quantities, is the basis of scientific research. Max Planck, the great German physicist, once said: "Everything which I can measure exists." However, as recent developments in physics have revealed, it is possible that a "thing" may exist which is so small that it cannot be measured by ordinary means. Indeed, in the later pages of our book we shall enter domains where precise measurements are no longer practicable. It is for this reason that we have added to our special equipment a "sense of imaginative abstraction" which will help us in studying phenomena about which the unaided physical senses can tell us nothing.

Contrary to popular belief, the latest theories of pure physics are *not* especially difficult to understand. The real difficulty lies in *be-*

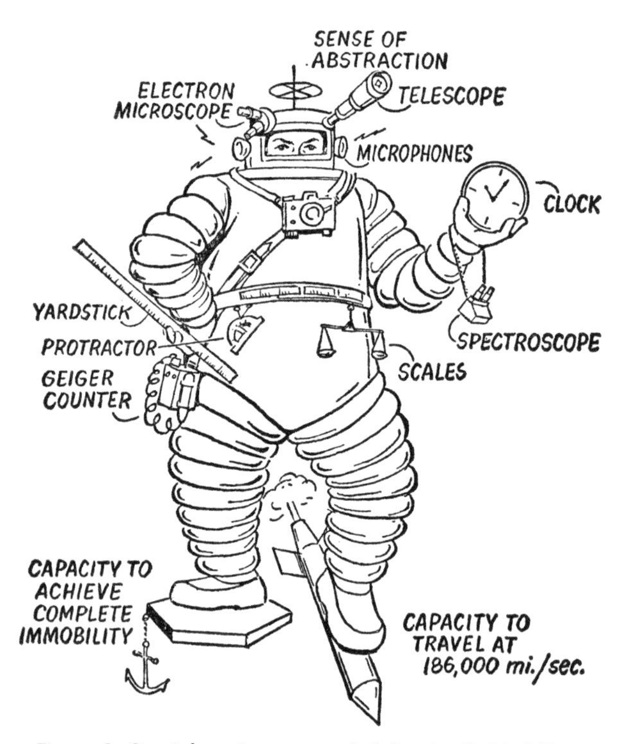

Figure 1. Special equipment needed for the Guided Tour.

lieving in them, for their amazing implications sometimes read like science-fiction.

We shall learn, for example, that the shortest distance between two points is *not* necessarily a straight line. (It is for you when you cross the street; it is not for light rays traversing tremendous distances through space.) In addition, we shall see that parallel lines may meet under certain circumstances and that space is actually *curved;* that the measurement of length and the passage of time are not always and everywhere the same; that yardsticks shrink and clocks slow down in systems which move with ultra-fast velocities.

Further, we shall learn why astronomers believe that the universe is expanding like a huge balloon; how physicists have proved that light can be subdivided into actual parts; and how we ourselves are not merely three-dimensional bodies existing in space, but that everything we do is intimately related to the fourth dimension—*time.* We shall also be finding out whether there are fifth, sixth, and even higher dimensions; and why the laws governing tiny atomic particles differ from those which rule the planets, stars and galaxies.

Perhaps most dramatic of all, we shall follow the implications of a theory introduced by a young patent clerk in 1904 when he stated that energy could actually be obtained from matter, and vice-versa. When at last, forty years later, artificial nuclear energy was produced by using his basic formulas, the entire world rang with the name of Albert Einstein.

CHAPTER △ TWO

MATTER AND MOTION

ABSOLUTENESS OR RELATIVITY?

LIGHT'S CONSTANT VELOCITY

Physics deals with phenomena in the world about us. These phenomena are so manifold that they stagger the imagination, yet physicists today assert that all of them are reducible to either matter or motion. Matter is everything that occupies space, and motion is commonly known as the act of changing place. No scientific definition could be more exact; however, it may help us to think of matter and motion in terms of a grammatical analogy. Matter is something substantial, a body, a *noun*. Motion may be thought of as that which acts, a *verb*.

Although this classification of phenomena into *motion* and *matter* may seem questionable to us, it was not so for primitive man. Archaic religions often made the distinction between *action* (the verb) and *substance* (the noun). For ages, science remained the secret of priests. It gained a more secular aspect only about 500 B.C. in ancient Greece, where philosophers performed the first systematic scientific researches, mostly by pure speculation. Their instruments were too primitive to encourage true experimentation. It was not until the 14th century that the empirical approach began to replace the merely speculative one.

In the early eighteen eighties, knowledge and technique had been perfected to a point where physicists could observe more and more phenomena they had been unable to perceive previously. Newly discovered facts were beginning to challenge the laws of nature which people for centuries had held to be true. Scientists had already experimented for some time with ultra-fast motion and had soon come to realize that tremendous velocities caused changes which could not be explained, either by logic or by the classical laws of motion as set forth by Isaac Newton.

In this connection, we may well ask: what is speed and what is velocity? *Speed* is the magnitude of motion, the act of moving swiftly, while *velocity* is the distance through which an object travels in a certain time. This latter concept thus includes not only magnitude but also the *direction* of motion.

Everyone, at some time or other, has noticed that speed is capable of playing queer tricks. When you look, for instance, through the window of a moving train you often cannot be sure whether another train you see nearby is moving or not.

Today we are aware that many such questions cannot be decided by visual observation alone. As a matter of fact, whether something is in motion or at rest can never be decided in this "optical" way. For centuries, however, people were convinced that the earth was motionless because, to them, it appeared so. Ptolemy, the Greek astronomer, left us an elaborate system in which a static earth is the center of the entire universe. Later, when Copernicus came to the conclusion that our earth is just another planet which revolves around the sun, he made his discovery by calculations, not by mere observation of this motion.

In beginning our study of motion, let's perform an experiment. Suppose you are riding on a train doing 70 miles an hour. You have been eating an apple and you want to get rid of the core. At first you thoughtlessly let it fall to the floor. Then your conscience begins to bother you. You pick it up and let it fall out of the window. Immediately you are struck by the fact that the core doesn't fall in as straight a line as it did to the floor. Rather, its fall looked to be slightly curved.

This, you might say, is just an illusion—and you would be right. The apple core only *appeared* to fall in a curve because your train did not move with a speed great enough to really alter the direction of a falling object. The velocity of the train was negligible in comparison with that of light, and it is only in the realm of such high velocities that directions are actually altered. Light rays advance, as is commonly known, with the greatest velocity which is possible in our material world, that is, 186,000 miles a second.

Now let's suppose that we have at our disposal a train which *is* able to advance with such speed. In order to find out whether the law which says that an object always falls in a straight line is right or wrong, we shall move the train at, say, 100,000 miles per second.

During this make-believe experiment (Fig. 2) the swiftly moving train shall be your system, or "frame of reference." The train which you board is also completely transparent so that I may observe everything which happens inside it, although I'll remain outside on an absolutely motionless platform. (No such platform exists in reality, but thanks to our special equipment we have one attached to one "leg" of our equipment.) This platform then becomes *my* system from which I'll observe *your* system. We agree beforehand that you will drop a small suitcase *inside* the train as you flash by the platform and we both shall watch how it falls.

When you drop the suitcase nothing unusual happens. Again, for you, like the apple core, it drops straight to the floor.

From where I was standing on the platform, however, the suitcase

Figure 2. A basic fact of Relativity. Things are different for someone in a high-velocity system than for someone in a system at rest.

seemed *not* to fall straight to the floor of the train, but described a curved line while falling.

You could repeat this experiment a hundred times—even transporting both systems to outer space where there is no air-resistance to reckon with—and the situation would be the same: a direction which is straight for you, is curved for me. Things look different, indeed, things *are* different, for someone in a high-velocity system than for someone in a system at rest. The reason for this is obviously because the latter system is motionless and does not participate in the motion of the fast system.

This basic fact of what has become known as *relativity* remained unnoticed for centuries because no one encountered it in ordinary life. Systems simply did not move fast enough to make alterations caused by speed noticeable. If men had been able to compare moving systems of such velocities, they would have realized long ago that phenomena exist in nature which cannot be judged independently. Such phenomena, if they are to make sense, can only be considered in connection with their environments and by comparison with each other.

With the recognition of relativity came a profound revelation. It meant that, contrary to Aristotle's teachings, the theory of the absolute was not a general law of nature. Uncontested for almost a thousand years, Aristotle's *Physics* began more and more to be challenged—especially when Galileo Galilei reputedly dropped a large cannon-ball and a small musket-ball from the leaning tower of Pisa, proving that, contrary to Aristotelian law, the two fell with the same speed. Yet the basis of Aristotle's thinking was the belief in absolute truths. This remained unchallenged until studies of high velocity systems made clear that so-called objective statements must often be replaced by subjective ones and absolute laws by relative ones.

CHAPTER △ THREE

WHAT IS RELATIVITY?

HIGH-VELOCITY SYSTEMS

"WORLD ETHER"

MICHELSON'S EXPERIMENT

Using our imaginary equipment, let's find out more about how things behave in extremely high-velocity systems.

Let's suppose that you travel in a jet-plane which advances with a quarter of the velocity of light. I then board a spaceship which is faster and we both measure from our separately moving systems a rocket that is even faster than your jet and my spaceship (Fig. 3).

Measuring the speed of the rocket from your jet, you discover that the rocket is going 100,000 miles a second. Yet, when I measure the velocity of the rocket from my spaceship, which is slower than the rocket yet faster than your jet, I find that the velocity of the rocket is only 80,000 miles per second.

The velocity of the rocket is less for me in my faster spaceship and more for you in your slower jet. Whose measurement is correct —yours or mine?

There is no judge in the universe who could decide this absolutely. This is what is meant by *relativity*. Put in a nutshell, relativity is the "it-all-depends-on-where-you-sit" idea.

Experimenting further, let us both stop at a motionless platform in space. Our rocket is still traveling there. When we measure its speed, we both find that it is 120,000 miles per second. Thus we have established the speed of the rocket to both our satisfactions because we performed the measurement together from the same motionless system.

There exists, however, no absolutely motionless system in nature.

For a long time scientists thought that such a system did exist. That is, they "postulated," or supposed, an absolutely motionless medium called "ether" through which they believed light rays traveled. This fluid-like substance was thought to be weightless and invisible; it filled all empty space in the entire universe. When scientists were dealing with tremendous speed, they leaned on this "immobile system" which made the absolute value of their motion-measurements unquestionable. The hypothesis of a motionless ether solved the velocity-measurement problems for them, just as the immobile platform did for us.

Yet scientists at this time were not aware that such problems existed. The concept of motion seemed to have been established once and for all. There were Aristotle's laws of motion which

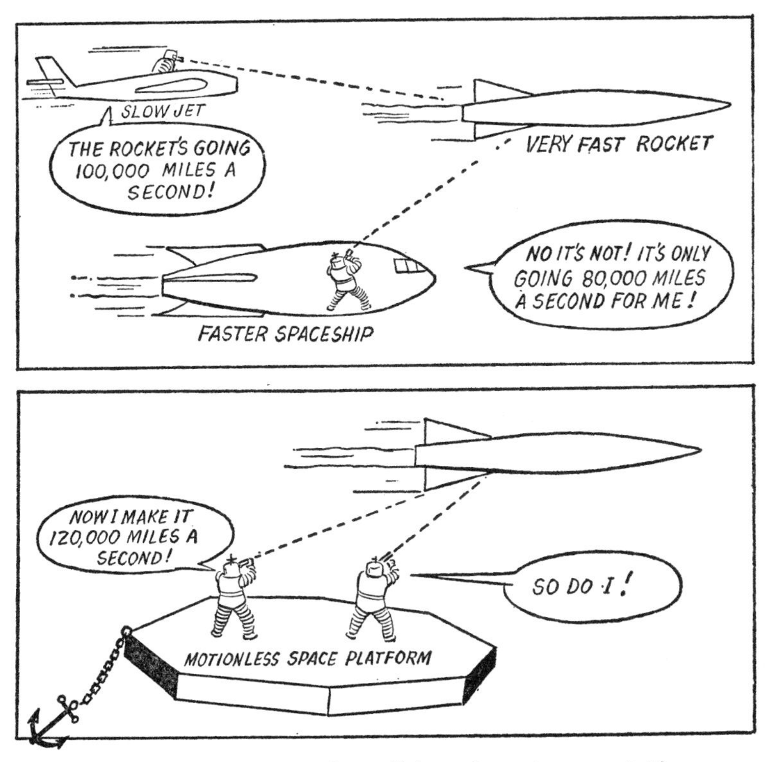

Figure 3. Relativity is just the it-all-depends-on-where-you-sit idea.

taught that the natural state of things is *rest.* Nothing moves unless it *is* moved, and the stronger the moving force, the faster the motion becomes.

The Aristotelian theory, which considers motion as pure accident, was modified in the 17th century by Newton. This English scientific genius stated that it is true that bodies remain at rest when not moved, but it is equally true that they continue their motion indefinitely unless they are stopped. Their motion is thus uniform in speed and continues in a straight line unless their speed and direction are altered by some external influence. Moreover, bodies are incapable of changing their state of rest or motion unless acted upon by outside forces.

Newton also considered that *force* is the power which changes the form and position of bodies, accelerates their motion, or stops them entirely. If the forces of acceleration, of mutual attraction between bodies, of resistance and of friction with other bodies are in balance, bodies are said to be in equilibrium or at rest.

Newton's laws of motion are dynamic laws which suppose that motion is the order of nature and is interrupted only by obstacles. But, just as Galileo's experiments challenged the teaching of Aristotle, Newton's mechanics modified Aristotle's laws, yet none of them contradicted the Aristotelian *principle of absoluteness.*

Newton's laws are not rejected by modern physicists. They are only modified in ultra-high-velocity systems. In daily life, however, where changes caused by great velocities are negligible, Newton's laws are perfectly adequate.

The notion of relativity did not originate with Albert Einstein. It was familiar even to Galileo. Unmoved by the doubts of his fellow scholars, he insisted that if we are inside a moving system, we have no way of determining the motion of this system; in fact, we are unable even to know whether our environment is moving at all because we participate in its motion. We experience this sensation every day when traveling up and down in elevators.

This tradition was preserved by such great scientists as Gottfried Leibniz; yet, the eventual realization that absolute physical laws must give way to the concept of relativity began much later and quite innocently in 1887 when two American physicists named Michelson and Morley decided to consider what effect the earth's motion would have on the velocity of light. In just a moment, we shall discuss their famous experiment.

The Aristotelian belief that light travels instantaneously, that it spreads in no time at all, was repudiated very early in scientific investigation. Galileo attempted to measure the speed of light with primitive instruments and did not succeed. The two lanterns with which he and an assistant tried to measure the speed of a beam of light one night were hardly far enough apart to permit an accurate measurement. Light propagates so incredibly fast that the expected delay in Galileo's experiment must have been about one hundred-thousandth of a second, which is quite unnoticeable to the human senses.

Galileo's observations of the moons of Jupiter, however, very probably gave inspiration to Olaus Römer when, in the 17th century, this Danish astronomer successfully measured light's velocity for the first time in history. Römer observed that the eclipses (obscurations of the Jovian moons) vary with the changing distances between Jupiter and the earth. When Jupiter and the earth were near to each other, the eclipses occurred earlier than when they were farther away. Römer concluded that this difference was caused by the amount of time it took light to travel these distances. By dividing the difference in distance, which was 186 million miles, by the time, which was 1000 seconds, Römer determined the velocity of light.

This figure of 186,000 miles per second was very close to the figure two later experimenters, Foucault and Fizeau, obtained in the 19th century by using mirrors; that is, in a non-astronomical way, employing terrestrial distances. Fizeau's light-source was not the sun but a candle whose light was made to travel to a mirror five miles away and then reflect back to a simple notched-wheel arrangement. The light ray made the ten miles (five out and five back) in the same time as Fizeau managed to turn his cogwheel, that is, in the same time as one empty gap between two teeth was followed by the next. In this first "laboratory experiment," Fizeau arrived at substantially the same figure for the velocity of light as had Römer.

Later Fizeau performed this same experiment in moving water and found that light's velocity was different. It appeared to him that when light traveled through swiftly-moving water its velocity was slightly faster than when it passed through air or a vacuum. Fizeau explained the discrepancy between these two measurements by the hypothesis that ether was thicker in material bodies like water than it was in a vacuum and, hence, would be traveling along *with* the moving water, together with the light which it was supposed to carry.

In Michelson's time, about thirty years later, it was still believed that not only did "ether streams" exist in liquids, but that "ether winds" must also exist in gases. Thus, Michelson reasoned, the earth itself, must cause an "ether wind" by its own motion, exactly as a fast-moving vehicle causes air currents in still air.

Determined to investigate the true nature of "ether winds," Michelson compared the velocities of light beams sent in mutually perpendicular directions (Fig. 4). He arranged two peripheral mirrors on a table at equal distances from a central mirror. This central mirror was covered with a semi-transparent layer of silver which admitted half of any ray shot toward it, while reflecting the other half. Thus a light ray coming from a pre-arranged light source was split into two light rays. Each of these, in turn, was reflected in the two mirrors, then united again at the central mirror. Both of the rays would eventually reach the eye of the experimenter at the same time, provided they were not influenced by ether winds.

At the arrival point Michelson placed an instrument sensitive to light. Now if Michelson's apparatus were completely motionless, the reflections in the mirrors would occur from equal distances and the experimenter's eye would see a bright spot at the central point of observation. If, however, one of the light beams traveled *across* and the other traveled *with* a supposed ether wind caused by the earth's motion, the brightness should have appeared shifted somewhat to one side.

Yet, no shift at all was noticed by Michelson, who repeated his experiment many times. The ether wind had apparently *not* influenced the two light beams.

Michelson thus found that there was *no difference* between the time it took the light beam to travel "*up*stream" and the time it took the light beam to travel "*cross*-stream." To assume that there was no ether wind because the earth was standing still would have been sheer nonsense. There was only one possibility left: the velocity of the two light beams *was the same* because the one did not travel "upstream" and the other did not travel "cross-stream," *for there were no such streams*. There were no "ether winds," because there was *no ether at all!*

This statement was contrary to everything scientists had previously believed in and started a crisis comparable to the Copernican revolution.

The non-existence of ether—that is, of an absolutely immobile

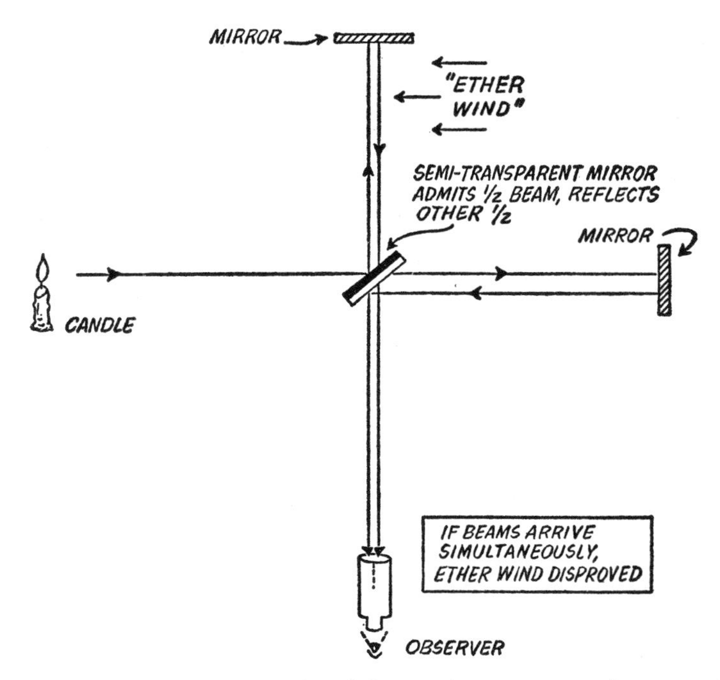

Figure 4. Principle of the famed Michelson-Morley experiment disproving the existence of "world ether."

substance—proved that there was no motionless system in nature. Everything is in motion, every system is a moving system, and there is no other way to define them except by comparing them with each other. The concept of absolute motionlessness, and, in consequence, the concept of "absolute motion," had to be abandoned and replaced by the concept of relative motions.

With the fall of the ether theory several questions immediately arose. Ether was supposed to be the medium transmitting light as it traveled through space. If this substance did not exist, then *how* and *in what* did light travel? This was an intriguing problem, yet another was even more so.

When light rays from the sun and from other celestial bodies were used in experiments, it turned out that they traveled with the same velocity. Regardless of how their celestial source moved, regardless of whether the earth (the system in which they were observed) was turning toward their source or away from it, they traveled with the same velocity—186,000 miles per second. Light thus appeared to possess a constant velocity. If it was true that all motion is relative, why was the velocity of light constantly the same? Why was it the *only* absolute value among relative ones?

The first possibility which emerged from this controversy was so improbable that scientists refused at first even to consider it. To reflect the light beams in his experiment, Michelson had used mirrors which were mounted on a table. Was it possible that the distance between the central mirror and peripheral mirror changed? That the table actually *shrank slightly* in the direction of the motion made by the earth through space? Was it imaginable that bodies themselves suffer at the hands of great speeds and that their own *dimensions* are thus relative?

Let us see for ourselves in the next chapter.

CHAPTER △ FOUR

OF SHRINKING YARDSTICKS

DIMENSIONS & SPACE

COORDINATES AND THE SKINDIVER

THE PYTHAGOREAN THEOREM

In order to find out whether bodies shrink when they are subjected to high velocities, let's measure some material object inside such a high-velocity system. Again, suppose this system is a transparent spaceship and you are aboard it.

Before you start and the spaceship is at rest, you take a yardstick and measure, inside the ship, the length of a small bench. You find that it is just 30 inches long when the ship is at rest. Let's see what happens when it travels with one-fifth of the velocity of light (Fig. 5).

The spaceship attains this speed and you measure the bench again. It is still 30 inches long!

"What's wrong?" you ask. "I thought that when my spaceship travels with such great speed the velocity is supposed to cause alterations in the length of bodies. The bench didn't shrink at all!"

Now suppose a friend, outfitted with the same equipment as ourselves, is on a motionless platform as the spaceship flies by. If your friend also measures the bench inside the spaceship from his immobile system, he finds that the bench *has* shrunk. It is no longer 30, but 29 inches long!

The bench shrank as a consequence of the ultra-fast motion in which it participated. But *you* could not notice this because you yourself participated in that motion, together with the yardstick with which you did your measuring. And the yardstick shrank, too, because it also participated in the motion of the system.

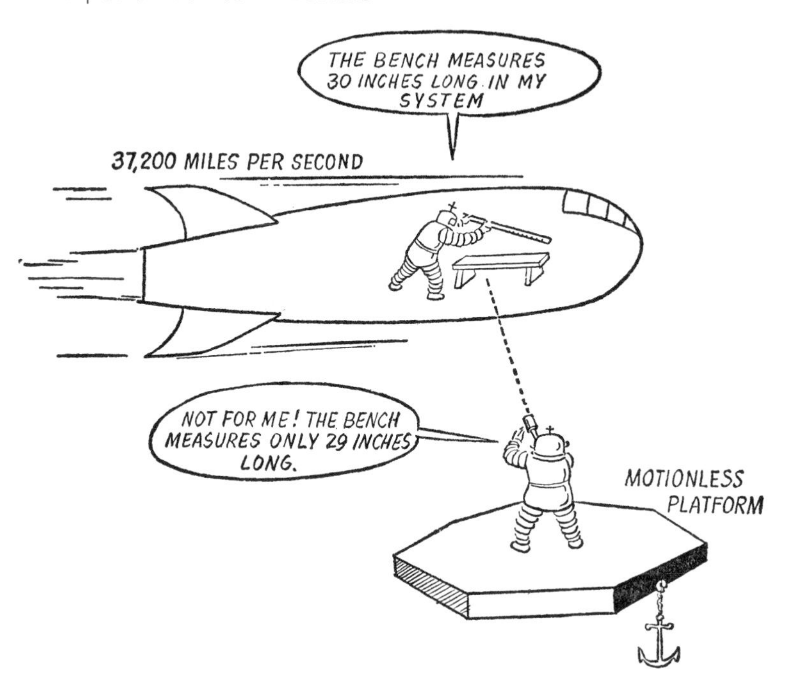

Figure 5. Dimensions are only relative concepts.

From this experiment we see that dimensions are indeed relative concepts. Yet, when this fact was first introduced by scientists, it stunned the world. Existing bodies in the physical universe had been classified since the dawn of science into solids, liquids and gases. Moreover, all of these, in whatever state, were considered to possess measurable properties like weight and mass. While it was true that for centuries many changes in the laws governing bodies had been made, no one in his right mind had ever before questioned the objective measurability of quantities. An object weighed so much, was so long, so wide, so high, and had a definite mass—and that was that.

Euclid's fundamental geometrical laws concerning dimensions were based on this principle. His so-called *axioms* started with the idea of "fixed points." Had anyone ever really seen these points? No. They are "ideal" or imagined points. You must simply believe in them as logical assumptions in understanding geometry, which is the science of measurement. Euclid stated that the distance between two points is marked by a line. This is the *linear* or first dimension: *length.* Remember that the points determining lines are not points you jot down on a paper with a pencil, but Euclidean points having no dimensions.

To define a certain line, it is enough to know only its length. Lines may be straight or curved. And Euclid also stated that the shortest distance between two points is a straight line. Later on we shall see whether he was entirely correct.

Combinations of lines form two-dimensional *plane* figures; for example, those you can draw on a sheet of paper, like triangles, circles, rectangles, or trapezoids. These have yet another dimension —*width.* So, to find the area of a plane figure it is not enough to know its length, you must also know how wide it is. Triangles, as you know, possess three angles which originate wherever the straight lines meet. Plane figures of various shapes and sizes may surround or determine what we call *bodies*—or three-dimensional material objects in space. Bodies, of course, have a third dimension —*height.* We need all three dimensions—length, width and height— to determine the *volume* of bodies.

When Newton described bodies, he thought of *material* bodies and based his theorems on the *material point.* Thus he gave a material counterpart to Euclid's ideal geometrical concept.

Now, three-dimensional bodies are located in *space;* consequently, space, to contain them, must be at least three-dimensional, too. What is space? Perhaps the best answer right now is to think of space as the void which contains everything, or rather as the emptiness in which bodies exist.

But, you might object, if space contains something, then it is no longer empty—and you would be right. Let's simply put it like this: space is everything that surrounds bodies. No one can determine what space is in a single sentence, but anyone can measure a part of it by using the same three data we already recognized as the characteristics of bodies: length, width, height. Real and palpable dimensions, of course, must be replaced by supposed ones because space itself cannot be seized with our hands and examined. However, with a set of these ideal lines we can measure the dimensions of space. These lines are called *axes* in order to distinguish them from the purely material dimensions of bodies themselves.

It is not necessary to calculate with each individual distance separately to determine distances in space. The well-known Pythagorean Theorem provides a shortcut for us by saying that the entire three-dimensional distance between two points is the square root of the sum of the squares of the individual distances. (In case you don't remember, the mathematical expression *square* means the quantity we obtain when multiplying something by itself. *Square root* is that quantity which produces a given other quantity when multiplied by itself. Thus, 3 is the square root of 9, because multiplied by itself it produces 9.)

At any rate, by setting up three mutually perpendicular axes you have "enclosed" that part of space you wish to examine. This must not be confused with "Galilean" space, because Galileo formed, from the concept of a concrete emptiness, the idea of abstract space. Nor is it "Newtonian" space either, where motion is absolute. It is just a part of space, the part you observe, the three-dimensional system you want to analyze. Descartes, the French philosopher, called this a *coordinate system.* The axes of such "Cartesian" coordinates are straight lines, and, just as there are planes and bodies, there are plane-and-space-coordinates. It is convenient to employ them when we want to determine something in a given part of space.

To give an illustration of how the Pythagorean Theorem provides a shortcut in locating certain distances in three-dimensional space, let us set up an actual problem. Imagine, therefore, a skindiver working underwater in a large botanical tank (Fig. 6). Standing at one corner of the tank, he sees a rare sea flower growing out of a rock some distance away in another part of the tank. His problem is to find out how far away the flower is from the point at which he is standing. Instead of awkwardly trying to measure across the tank to find this distance, he decides to use mathematics. By looking

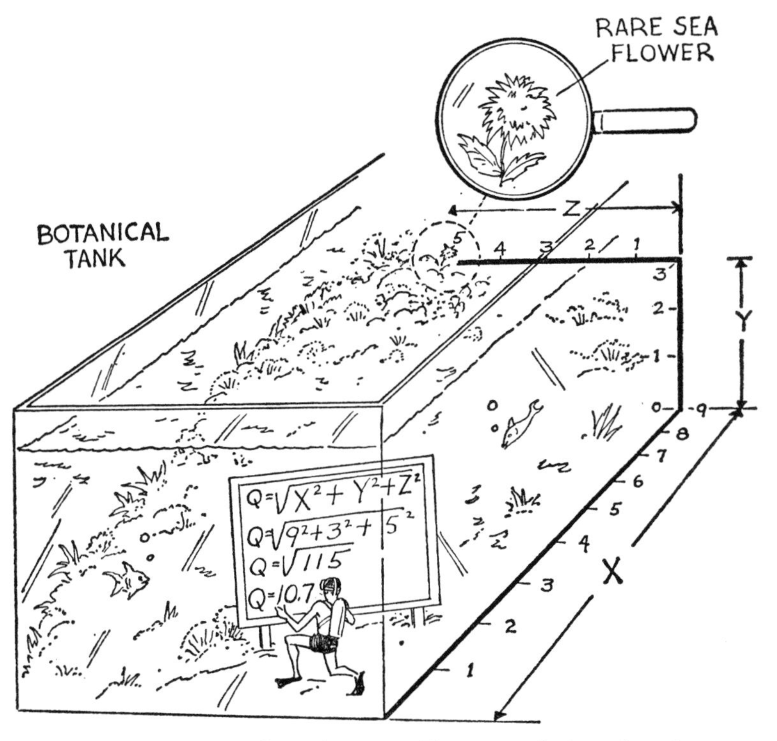

Figure 6. Skindiver using the Pythagorean Theorem to find out how far away he is from the rare sea flower.

at Figure 6, you will see that the skindiver is actually standing at the zero point of a coordinate system formed by the sides of the tank. Realizing that he can get the answer to his problem by finding the square root of the sum of the squares of the individual distances on the coordinates, he determines the distance along the X axis to be 9 yards, the height of the flower along the Y axis to be 3 yards, and the lateral distance along the Z axis to be 5 yards. The actual distance he wishes to determine he arbitrarily calls Q. Having his values, he proceeds to work out the problem from the formula:

$$\sqrt{X^2 + Y^2 + Z^2} = Q$$

Substituting the values, he gets:

$$\sqrt{9^2 + 3^2 + 5^2} = Q$$

$$\sqrt{81 + 9 + 25} = Q \text{ or,}$$

$$\sqrt{115} = Q$$

Now, extracting the square root to a near approximation, the skin-diver finds that his actual distance away from the rare sea flower is:

10.7 yards

Unfortunately, all use of coordinate systems is not as simple as this; we shall learn more about them later. Right now, it is enough to say that the inside of your spaceship, which traveled so fast that it shrank—together with everything that was in it—was, in a way, also a coordinate system. There, you, being inside that system, could not notice this alteration in dimension.

Physicists who tried to explain the negative results of Michelson's experiment also wished to preserve traditional theories, at the same time proposing others to answer the undeniable results of that experiment. Fitzgerald suggested that the shrinking might be only a simple mechanical effect, a by-product of ultra-fast motion. But H. A. Lorentz, a Dutch mathematician, boldly stated that anything moving with such high velocity would shrink in the direction of its motion; mathematically this resulted in the famous "Lorentz transformation equations." These equations tell how much length is affected by any given velocity.

As a result of Lorentz's work particularly, a number of baffling questions arose. Was contraction caused by high velocities a universal phenomenon? Did space itself also shrink as material bodies do when subjected to ultra-fast motion? Or did bodies shrink just because they were imbedded in shrinking space?

Albert Einstein was to provide the answers to these questions in his Theory of Special Relativity by introducing *time* as a variable, relative quantity. The same theory was also to solve the apparent contradiction between the principle of relativity and the law of propagation of light. In fact, the velocity of light, which is independent of the motion of its system, was to become the yardstick of the new world of relativity.

Indeed, scientists and astronomers were badly in need of such a space-measuring unit, for if such vast distances (as from one star to another) were described in terms of ordinary miles, several thousands and even millions of zeros would be necessary. That is why astronomers today speak in terms of the *light year,* or the distance which light travels in one year. Remember also that in speaking of light's *velocity* the concept of time as well as space is included. It became Einstein's greatest objective to focus his attention on the concept of time.

Before we get acquainted with the experimental proofs of Einstein's theory, however, we must find out whether its mainstay, the velocity of light, is really constant under all circumstances.

CHAPTER △ FIVE

THE ENIGMA OF LIGHT

LIGHT'S CONSTANT VELOCITY

WAVE VS. PARTICLE THEORY

PROPERTIES OF LIGHT

To find out whether light is an "exception," that is, whether its velocity is unconditionally constant and independent of its source and the systems in which it is observed, let's suppose that you are traveling with the velocity of light. As no material body can do this, let's pretend that you are actually a light ray propagating through outer space (Fig. 7). A less speed-conscious friend will travel with only half that velocity in a spaceship.

Now, if you, as a light ray, were to hitch a ride on your friend's spaceship, wouldn't you become a super-fast light ray? Obviously the answer should be yes, because you would be adding *your* speed to that of your friend's.

As a light ray you possess, before you board the spaceship, a velocity of 186,000 miles per second, as all light does. The velocity of your friend's spaceship is 93,000 miles per second.

186,000 miles per second
93,000 miles per second
279,000 miles per second

By all logic you should now be a light ray traveling at 279,000 miles per second.

But what happens? When you measure your velocity with respect to the system of the spaceship it is *still* 186,000 miles per second—no more, no less.

Have we made a mistake? We have not, for nothing can increase the velocity of a light ray. The velocity of light is independent of

Figure 7. No additional velocity can increase the velocity of light.

the system in which it travels and in which it is measured. It remains 186,000 miles per second regardless of whether the system is moving with considerable speed like your friend's ship, whether the system stands almost still, or whether it is entirely motionless like our space-platform of an earlier chapter.

Our equipment also tells us that light's velocity is independent of its source. A light ray, for example, coming from a lamp on our motionless space-platform would propagate with the same velocity as a light ray originating from the searchlight of a spaceship in flight.

Now why is this substance or force, or whatever it is, so reluctant to behave in a relative manner, as do all other natural phenomena? What *is* light anyway?

Since pre-historic times man has been puzzled by the phenomenon of light. Some thought that light was a flame from the sun, others that it was actually a stream emanating from the eye. In any case, light appeared to cause whiteness as well as other colors and its absence caused darkness, and all this without exercising any observable action. This is why the problem of light was a mysterious one from the very beginning.

There have been many light theories, yet all of them characterized light as different from any other phenomenon. Unlike material bodies which man can touch or sense through their properties, light remained something immaterial and intangible.

The discovery of the telescope, which was first used for scientific purposes by Galileo, brought faraway things nearer. As the phenomenon of light was always closely connected with man's ability to see, light itself became a subject of intense study. When Galileo tried to measure light's speed, he dealt the first blow to its elusiveness.

The more men studied light, the more they wondered what its true nature might be. Was light actually a body or some kind of "force"? The realistic Newton entirely rejected the classification of light as a matterless phenomenon: "It is arbitrary to say," he insisted, "that light is an exception among existing things. Light consists of small particles, or corpuscles, which are emitted in straight lines from such luminous sources as the sun or a lamp."

Although in his own time Newton's theories were not often doubted, this one was challenged almost immediately by Christian Huyghens. This Dutch astronomer stated his own theory with equal conviction:

"Light is not an 'object' like physical bodies. Light is a *function,* the process of waviness! Light waves move like water waves which are produced when a stone is dropped into a lake."

To this, the defenders of Newton's particle theory asked: "If water waves travel in water, through what medium does light travel?" This question could not be answered by existing, proved facts. As so often is the case, when no facts are available, scientists turned to a *hypothesis* which would fit the theory. Hence, they conveniently created "world ether," which provided a mediatory substance through which light waves could propagate. We have seen in an earlier chapter the fate of the ether hypothesis. Yet at the time of its creation physicists who believed in the ether theory had good reason to do so. The ether concept supported the wave theory and this theory explained much more adequately the essential properties of light than did the particle theory.

Among the properties of light which supported the wave theory is the *reflection* of light rays. (See Figure 8.) If, argued the growing number of wave-partisans, you throw heavy objects at a mirror they rebound or may even break the mirror. But if you shoot light

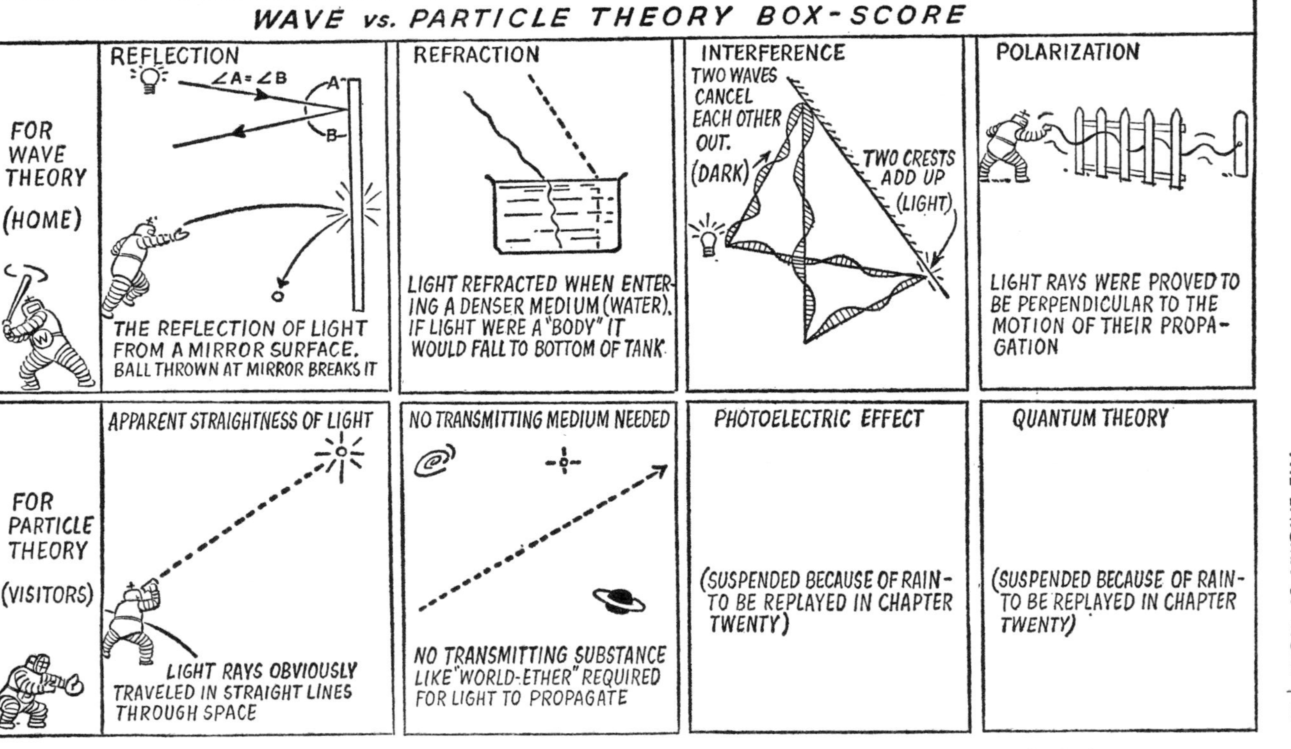

Figure 8. A Wave vs. Particle Theory "box-score" showing the major arguments supporting both theories.

rays at a mirror they do not rebound in the mechanical way objects do, but are reflected according to optical laws.

In the phenomenon known as *refraction,* light rays are bent as they pass through transparent liquids such as water. If, argued the wave-theorists, light were a body, it would simply fall to the bottom of a container of water.

In the particle theory's favor, however, was the apparent straightness of light rays. Today, it is an observed fact that waves do *not* always travel in straight lines. But, in attempting to explain the contradiction of straightness and waviness, the wave theorists could furnish only a complicated supposition based on the addition of several waves which would form a straight line in the "ether sea." Meanwhile, straightness seemed to be, in the particle theory, a simple mechanical characteristic.

Perhaps the strongest argument supporting the wave theory of light was the phenomenon of *interference,* first observed experimentally by Thomas Young about 1800. If two light rays are combined, one would assume that they reinforce each other; that is, two light rays should produce twice as much illumination as one. Yet, this was not always found to be true, for their meeting sometimes causes darkness. To this, the particle theory had no answer. Two bodies were always more than one.

Yet, to the wave theorists, this interfering of waves made sense. When the crests of one light wave cut through the troughs of another light wave, mutual annihilation occurs at these points and hence all light is canceled out.

However, this same phenomenon of interference raised the first serious doubts in the ether concept when Fresnel, a young French engineer, discovered another phenomenon of light—*polarization.* He found that the motion of light waves is not longitudinal, that is, it does not take place in the direction of propagation in gases and other such immaterial substances as ether was supposed to be. Instead, he showed that light waves are *transverse* like the waves produced when one attempts to shake a rope between the slats of a fence. This means that they are perpendicular to the direction of their propagation. Ether was considered to be emptiness. If it could not be admitted that this emptiness was some sort of liquid or solid material body, the entire ether theory was reduced to absurdity.

Exactly that became the case after Michelson's experiment. Yet scientists still had to face the same old problem. If there is no ether, in what do light rays travel and how do light rays perform the process of waving? And if light consists of particles, how could one explain the complicated phenomena of optics, such as reflection, refraction, interference and polarization?

Denying the wave theory would have meant the rejection of something whose exact properties had been proved and measured. *Wavelength,* or the distance between two "wave crests," for example, had become the accepted unit of light measurement and those familiar with radio also know that *frequency*—the number of wave-vibrations per second—is equal to the velocity of the wave motion divided by this wavelength.

Today we realize that *both* wave and particle theories are correct. Light consists of tiny bundles, which *behave* like waves.

The following is a particularly apt description of the phenomenon we call light: *

> Unlike sound, light does not require a material medium for its propagation. Although it may pass through many kinds of media, it does a better job getting around in a vacuum than anywhere else. Its speed is incredible. Nothing can outrun it. Very few velocities can approach it. Its method of getting from place to place is still a mystery. Somewhere within an atom or molecule, light energy has its origin. Somewhere within another molecule or atom it ends its existence. Between these two atoms or molecules it is light, hurtling through space at the tremendous speed of 186,000 miles/sec. If it strikes a reflecting surface, it changes direction in less than a trillionth of "the twinkling of an eye," and is off again with the same incredible speed. When it strikes a substance through which it may pass, it reduces speed slightly and then continues on its way. If something in its path stops it, it ceases to be light.

* Frank M. Durbin, *Introduction to Physics.* Englewood Cliffs, N. J.: Prentice-Hall, Inc., 1955.

CHAPTER △ SIX

THE REALM OF FORCES

ELECTROMAGNETISM

FORCE FIELDS

THE LANGUAGE OF MATHEMATICS

The arguments in favor of the wave theory of light were so convincing that scientists did their best to hang on to this theory. *Sounds,* for example, or the vibrations transmitted through a material medium which affect the organ of hearing, were definitely proven to travel in wave-like form. In fact sound waves, formed by the condensations and rarefactions in the air, are longitudinal and require a transmitting medium; otherwise, they could not exist. On the moon, for instance, you would probably hear nothing if a friend yelled to you; because of the practically airless lunar atmosphere, sound would have nothing in which to transmit itself. Therefore, communication on the moon's surface will almost surely be by radio. Now radio, or electromagnetic waves, can travel through a vacuum without benefit of any medium, just as light propagates through empty space.

What is *electromagnetism* as we know it today? A simple answer is that it is *something* consisting of electricity and magnetism. Let us examine these components one by one.

Magnetized iron or *lodestones* which attracted certain metals were known for centuries to sailors. They were used as compasses because of their property of pointing north and south. They behaved in this manner because the earth itself is a huge magnet with north and south magnetic poles which repel the like poles of compasses and attract the unlike ones.

The fact that certain forms of iron became magnetized when

brought near a magnet indicated that magnetism existed not only *inside* the magnet but also around it. Indeed, scientists observed that magnetic forces around a magnetized bar caused iron filings to form distinct lines. These lines marked the path of magnetic forces about the magnet and were called *force lines*. The environment of the magnet, or that area where these invisible force lines existed, was called a *magnetic force field*.

Were similar phenomena observed around electrified bodies? Although we are accustomed to dealing with electricity as a current traveling through conductors, you may have heard the story of the Greek sailor who rubbed a piece of amber with a bit of fur and found that it attracted bits of straw. He called this amber "elektron," and from thence comes our word electricity. Even from this we learn that electricity can travel without a conductor or any other intermediary, just as magnetism does. Furthermore, electrically charged bodies attracted unlike charged bodies and repelled like ones. The two kinds of electricities were called positive (+) and negative (−) by Benjamin Franklin, inventor of the lightning rod. Charles de Coulomb later was able to measure the electric forces which exist between two electrically charged bodies, and called them *electrostatic forces*. He found that these forces are directly proportional to the amount of charge of the two bodies and inversely proportional to the square of the distance which exists between them. The effect of one electric charge on another is transmitted along *lines of forces* in the space between them, or in the so-called *electrical force field*.

This phenomenon was soon recognized to be very similar to the one observed in magnetism. Yet the actual link between magnetism and electricity was not discovered until the first quarter of the 19th Century when Rowland and Oersted observed that conductors carrying electrical currents are surrounded by magnetic fields. Subsequently it was proved that electrically charged bodies, if they are moving, create magnetic fields about themselves. No magnetic fields, however, were observable when these bodies stood still—that is, when they were not charged.

Still another step forward was made when the French physicist

André Ampère determined the principle of the electromagnet—the production of magnetic fields by electric currents.

The logical question then was, if electricity produces magnetic fields, does a magnet likewise produce electric currents? It was Michael Faraday's great discovery that it does. He observed first that a wire carrying an electric current rotated about a magnet. Then he saw that electric currents were generated in the wire when he moved it past the magnet. Faraday thus discovered the principles governing electric motors and dynamos, but even more important, he connected the two. He stated that both a magnet and a current-carrying wire were surrounded by force fields, and the effect of magnetism on electricity and the effect of electricity on magnetism were results of an interaction between the two fields which together form the *electromagnetic field.*

This discovery touched off a series of events which was to change our conception of the Universe. Electromagnetic fields are not visible, and instruments capable of discovering anything about them were not available in Faraday's time. Let us, however, with the aid of our super-microscope, take a magnetic bar and see what happens about it (Fig. 9). We can actually follow the force lines of the magnetic field—the paths which like and unlike charges must pursue when obeying the laws of attraction and repulsion.

Now if we shift our gaze to a current-carrying conductor, the

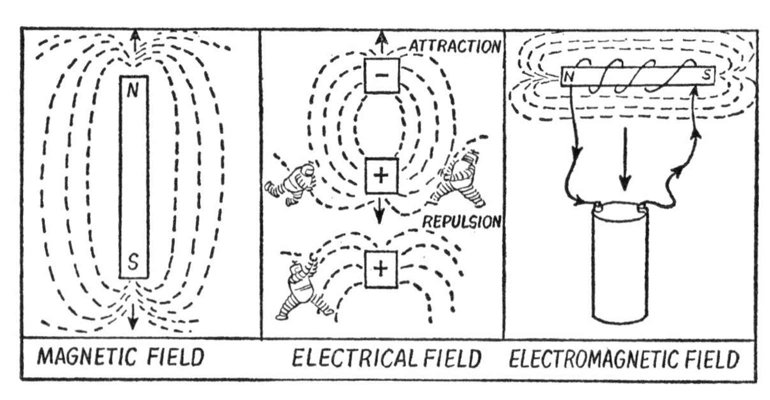

Figure 9. Force fields.

view will be similar. Next, a glance at a charged electric conductor turning about a magnet is sufficient for us to see that a current is always induced when the flux of magnetic lines going through a circuit is changed. Another glance convinces us that electric currents indeed originate when the flux of magnetic lines are alternately cut across by an electrified circuit.

Perhaps it was fortunate that Faraday was not a trained mathematician, for had he concerned himself with geometrical presentations of physical laws he might never have established the concept of electromagnetic fields. Furthermore, these mutually interacting fields were not physically provable as material bodies and hence might have been strongly doubted by capable physicists. Such fields could only be described as "somethings" which were neither enclosed by Euclidian planes nor themselves contained such bodies. Yet, being transversed by these mysterious force lines, neither could they be merely empty space. Here science was confronted with two "non-material substances"—electrical and magnetic fields—which could mingle with each other and yet not destroy each other. How could such apparent enigmas be satisfactorily defined or even talked about?

Finally, it remained for James Clerk Maxwell to write down a series of equations which clothed Faraday's field concepts in decent mathematical garb. Without the use of a single instrument, but with only pencil, paper and his good Scottish brain, he laid down one of the mightiest cornerstones of modern physics. Indeed it was all of twenty-three years later before his equations defining electromagnetic fields were experimentally verified by Heinrich Hertz, a German physicist. Many practical applications of them followed, including the discovery of wireless telegraphy and radio waves.

Maxwell's contributions thus reinforced the age-old belief that human thinking is able to predict facts long before they are discovered. He was not the first, however. The great significance of Newton's work is that, in addition to his actual physical discoveries, he gave precise mathematical descriptions of his physical laws. Some of these laws have since been challenged and improved, yet

Newton's equations gave rise to the important new branch of science, mathematical physics, a tool without which modern scientific research would be paralyzed.

The very purpose of using mathematical symbols in physics is to present phenomena, their actions and interactions, in a clearer manner than lengthy descriptions can do. Whenever specific characteristics of the things we are dealing with are not important to the problem in question, we replace them by their quantities. Thus, whether we discuss chairs or houses makes no particular difference. Instead of speaking of two chairs and three houses, we go to a more general classification and speak of five objects or "bodies." In cases where precise numerical values are unimportant, a further step toward "depersonalization" is to replace the concept of objects by signs; for example, by the first letters of our alphabet when we know our objects, and by the last letters of the alphabet when we do not. Thus a, b, and c, are used to signify known values or quantities; x, y, and z, unknown ones. In expressing relationships between these so-called algebraic symbols, we use *formulas.* We call *equations,* on the other hand, statements of equality between certain known and certain unknown quantities. Formulas have been called "short-hand versions" of laws reigning in nature, since all that exists in nature, known or not yet known, is more and more recognized as having some definite mathematical form. Maxwell's confirmation of Faraday's field concepts, as we have just seen, is a perfect illustration of this.

Now, when Faraday unconsciously broke with the Newtonian theory of describing bodies as discontinuous units or "material points" which acted upon each other at a distance, he really proved that it was not necessary to postulate such interactions. He showed this by the introduction of continuous fields where uninterrupted and never-ending actions were present. Maxwell, in attempting to translate this experimental fact into the language of mathematics, was faced with the problem of finding a mathematical expression which would describe unbroken and continuous processes. a, b, c or x, y, z represented generally distinct and discontinuous units in equations. A different mathematical language was needed to express continuous action, and this was provided for in the *differential calculus* (actually invented earlier by Newton or Leibniz, or both).

Unbroken actions and/or changes in space are geometrically represented by points which follow each other in infinite closeness. The differential calculus tells the same story of continuity in the language of mathematics. It marks differences, too small to be expressed separately, by adding *prime marks* (′, ″, ‴, etc.) to the already named quantity. Thus, Y' differs only slightly from Y, Y'' only slightly from Y''', and so forth. Differential calculus thus indicates the rate of change of variable quantities.

Does this seem complicated? Not if you will think of a certain color, say red. There are many different shades of red, among them pink, crimson, scarlet, ruby, rose. What happens? Eventually we run out of names for the different intensities of redness. There are no names, for example, for the shades of red as they change from rose to pink. Now, where semantics fails us, mathematics does not. This is the great achievement of the calculus. Using mathematical symbols, it is capable, in effect, of telling us at which points rose is changed from less rose and less rose to more pink, more and more pink—and finally to pink itself.

Maxwell used exactly this approach in order to present in an adequate mathematical form the continuous lines of forces and the incessant interaction between bodies, even when these bodies are the smallest particles possible in nature.

But Maxwell, who so precisely described the *behavior* of these particles, did not provide a theory for the particles *themselves!* The exact description of such a particle has no place in his field-presentation. It remained, in this continuous concept, as discontinuous a material point as Newton's mechanics had presented it.

Maxwell further observed that the equations with which he determined the strength of these force fields were exactly the same ones which describe a wave formed by a vibrating string or a sound wave traveling through the air. This meant that these electromagnetic forces were also traveling in the form of waves in the electromagnetic field.

Using his equations, Maxwell was able to calculate the speed with which the electromagnetic forces—now determined to be electromagnetic waves—travel. And this speed was found to be exactly equal to that of light! Could light, then, be a kind of electromagnetic wave? Were *all* waves of this velocity somehow related?

Indeed it was subsequently proved that light, considered for so long to be a unique phenomenon, actually has many relatives. When Hertz succeeded in demonstrating the existence of electromagnetic waves, he also proved—exactly as predicted by Maxwell—that other radiations spread with the same velocity. Many of these types of radiations are not visible because their wavelengths are different from that of light and our eyes are incapable of registering them. The very reason why we see light, including all the colors of the visible spectrum, is because only certain of these varying wavelengths are responded to by the human retina. Actually, the portion of radiation we are capable of seeing is proportionately very small compared to the range taken in its entirety. We cannot, for example, see very long wavelengths like radio waves or very short ones like ultra-violet rays, although we know that they are there.

All of these radiations, light included, do not require an intermediary substance in which to propagate. Thus the field theory helped to eliminate the ether hypothesis.

The triumph of the wave theory of light, reinforced by the field aspect, was overwhelming in the last years of the past century. Scientists knew of course that several problems were still unsolved —among them the apparent straightness of light rays—however, no one doubted that all of these problems would eventually be solved within the framework of the wave theory.

Also, the contradiction between the constant velocity of light (as well as other radiations) and the relativity of velocities in other moving systems still persisted. Yet no one at the time could have foreseen the brilliant way in which Einstein's theories of relativity were to solve these problems. Moreover, scientists would have been even more surprised to learn that the particle theory of light, which seemed to have been buried for good, was soon to reappear and that Max Planck was to present its new version in his Quantum Theory.

Actually, Einstein presented the Theory of Relativity some five years after Planck's announcement concerning the theory of light quanta. However, subsequent developments of the Quantum Theory cannot be properly understood without first knowing something about the Theory of Relativity. We shall examine it more closely in our next chapter.

CHAPTER △ SEVEN

SPECIAL RELATIVITY

SIMULTANEITY

THE RELATIVITY OF TIME

When Einstein's name is mentioned, many of us associate it with the man who first stated that time is a relative concept. What exactly did Einstein mean by this?

To find out, let's suppose—with the aid of our special equipment—that you and I are a pair of space explorers watching for two light rays from outer space in order to determine whether they arrive simultaneously or not. For this purpose we have placed two mirrors, A and B, at opposite ends of a very long space balloon. The balloon is at rest, and is so long that it would take considerable time even for a light ray to travel its entire length. We agree beforehand that you will stand halfway between the two mirrors, in the exact center of the balloon, which we will call your *stationary system of reference* (Fig. 10).

At the same time, I board a very fast spaceship which advances with uniform velocity parallel to your balloon. When the light rays arrive from outer space I shall be at the exact center of the balloon, just opposite you, and will observe the same two rays from my *high-velocity system.*

Remember that we are in empty space, far from the earth or any other celestial body which might have an effect on our observations.

When the two light rays arrive, you establish with your time equipment that they arrive at exactly the same time.

"The two rays," you report, "struck both mirrors simultaneously at precisely 3 o'clock."

However, in observing the two light signals from my high-velocity

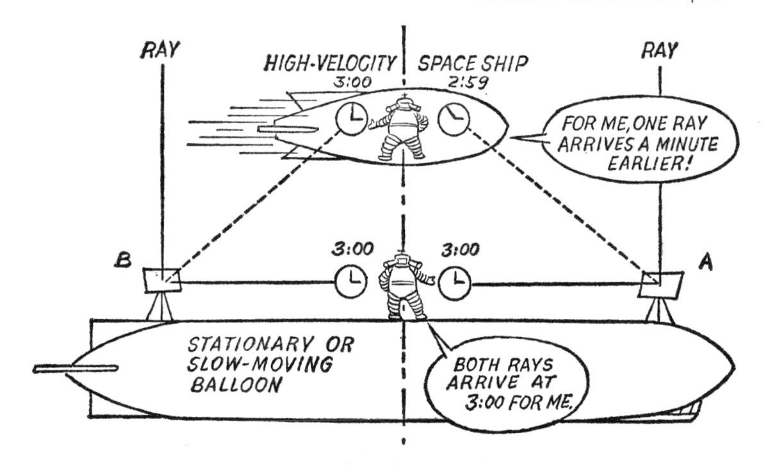

Figure 10. The relativity of time.

system, I notice that they do not arrive simultaneously at the two mirrors in your stationary system.

"Mirror B," I report, "was struck at 3 o'clock, but mirror A was struck earlier—at 2:59!"

Being already acquainted with alterations caused by high velocities, we suspect that the discrepancy between our observations has something to do with this phenomena, for your system was at rest like the mirrors, while mine moved with tremendously high velocity. In any case, the arrival of the two light rays was simultaneous for you but not for me. Thus we have determined that time, like space, is also altered by the velocity of the frame of reference in which it is observed.

Since we know, however, that there exists no absolutely motionless system in nature, let us cause your balloon-system to advance in the same direction and parallel to my spaceship. Its velocity is also uniform, yet is much slower than mine. Now we are two observers whose systems are moving *relative* to one another. You adjust your observation devices so that you again observe the arrival of the two light signals simultaneously and I do the same with my equipment. But, since the velocity of our systems is different, we could never observe *together* the two events as being simultaneous for both of us. When they occur at the same time for you, they do not occur at the same time for me and vice versa. Unless our velocities are the same, your concept of simultaneity will never be the same as mine.

Having concluded our experiment, we both stop at a space station for refreshment. Curiously, you are very hungry but I am not.

"We spent only a few seconds up there," I remark.

"A few seconds?" you reply, astonished. "You mean several hours, don't you?"

Why the difference in our appetites? Because for you, time flowed more rapidly than for me, especially if your speed was slow compared to the velocity of light and if mine closely approximated the velocity of light. From the standpoint of my high-velocity system not only my clock, but all time processes, even the biological ones like digestion, would slow down.

Suppose we had spent, in terms of earth time, several years in our respective vehicles. Would I descend from mine much younger than you from yours? Would I, in effect, be experiencing the same time adjustment as Lt. Farnsworth of Chapter One? If I had spent, let us say, one hundred terrestrial years in such a high-velocity spaceship, would I be able to return, still young, in time to celebrate the wedding of a great-great-grandchild?

This might very well be the case. Einstein's Theory of Special Relativity demonstrated that in the case of high velocity, time behaves like space; both wane under such conditions.

Such a journey, however, can only be imagined; the chances of its ever happening in reality are very slim indeed. Why? Because nothing in actuality moves with *constant velocity.* True, it could move with constant *speed* because this means that its speed is permanently the same, but constant velocity means that speed *and* direction remain unchanged.

To illustrate, if we had been two real space travelers, this differential in our time processes would not have been permanently changed, even if we had traveled with these high speeds, because our take-offs and landings would have meant accelerating and decelerating. The constancy of our velocity would have been interrupted. Not even in space could we have kept our velocity constant because we could not have maintained a uniformly straight direction in a universe containing celestial bodies and force fields, which would have influenced our motion.

Einstein for several reasons, one being that the demonstration of his new laws was rendered less complicated, described in his Theory of Special Relativity only cases of straight-lined, uniform motion. He reserved for his Theory of General Relativity the discussion of all other kinds of motion.

It is these special cases that we may observe experimentally with our imagined equipment. Thus we could assert that you, in your stationary balloon and/or slow-moving balloon, had another concept of time than I had in the high-velocity system where my "clock" slowed down, thus altering my time sense. Now your balloon, or my spaceship (in fact, any vehicle or moving system), possesses its own time, just as it possesses its own length, width and height. This is the same as saying that any system has its own particular *time dimension* as well as the particular space dimensions which characterize it.

To state therefore that two events occur at the same time makes sense only if we know where they are observed, and *relative to what* moving system they are simultaneous. In other words, we must know the velocity of the frame of references *from which* and also *of which* we measure time.

Time data are thus not independent from the systems in which they are established. The concept of absolute time, universal and the same everywhere (Newtonian or "objective" time), does not exist! In the same manner as absolute space, the notion of absolute time was replaced by the new concept of relativity.

Now if time, like space, is influenced by velocity, reasoned Einstein, it is natural that anything we measure by space- and time-measuring units—whether by yardsticks or clocks—appears to be altered even if the measured phenomena is constant like the velocity of light. It was in this way that Fizeau was deceived in his calculation of the velocity of light when he measured its passage through a swiftly moving liquid. Actually it was not the velocity of light that changed in his experiment but the devices themselves with which he measured it.

The Theory of Special Relativity proves this fundamental law of nature by mathematical means. How?

If you would like to know how Einstein arrived at the same conclusion as we did earlier in our space vehicles (and without the aid of the equipment at our command on this Tour), pay close attention to what follows because the Theory of Relativity is probably one of the most unorthodox chapters in the history of pure science.

When doubts arose in the concept of ether and the inherent idea of an absolutely motionless system of reference, the need became great for replacing it with a frame of reference for measurements in which high velocities were involved. Finally, in 1904, Henri Poincaré, a French philosopher, made this statement:

"It is certain that we cannot determine motion in an absolute way. However, phenomena of nature must be the same for two observers who move *relative* to one another. This *principle of relativity* requires new laws of motion. Since no velocity can exceed that of light, these new dynamics must be characterized in terms of this natural law."

A year later Albert Einstein, then a young patent-office clerk, presented these new dynamics in his Theory of Special Relativity. The ideas contained in this celebrated paper were revolutionary and difficult to accept, not only because they challenged centuries-old scientific theories, but also because they could not be proved by direct experiment.

True, Fitzgerald and Lorentz had come to the conclusion that the dimensions of bodies are altered by ultra-fast motion. The transformation equations of Lorentz furnished an adequate mathematical description of this. However, this could not be proved by material means, for any measuring device, being a material body itself, would shrink exactly in proportion as the body to be measured. For a time, there was hope that this could be done by electrical means because particles in electrically-charged high-velocity systems readjusted their positions, that is, were more tightly compressed, so that Lorentz's predicted contraction was produced.

When, after Poincaré's statement that determination of absolute motion by *any* experimental processes was impossible, physicists concentrated on the study of a working hypothesis of relativity.

It was understood that this hypothesis must rest on the proven fact of the constancy of light's velocity. Accordingly, Einstein set forth to demonstrate how this law, instead of being contrary to the principle of relativity, is in reality the cornerstone of it.

CHAPTER △ EIGHT

"WHERE ARE THE SNOWS OF YESTERYEAR?"

IMAGINARY QUANTITIES

THE MYSTERIOUS $\sqrt{-1}$

EINSTEIN'S *t* AXIS

FOUR-DIMENSIONAL DISTANCE

THE SKINDIVER AGAIN

Confined to a single sentence, Einstein's problem was to find *the unknown factor* by which one observer in one system, moving relative to another observer in another system, could readjust his space and time devices (his yardsticks and clocks) to measure light's constant velocity of 186,000 miles per second so that there would be no difference between them from the viewpoint of such measurements.

In other words, space and time were to be determined in a relativistic way. Scientists, we have learned, use *coordinates* to determine distances in space. To measure space, Einstein employed straight-lined Cartesian space coordinates with X, Y, and Z axes to mark length, width and height respectively.

In order to measure in time, too, Einstein needed a similar device. Time, however, is different from space. You are not talking about the same thing, for example, when you say "far away in Spain" and "way back in the 'Twenties." Physicists, by presenting natural phenomena in terms of mathematical abstractions, do so in a far more exact manner than in such verbal descriptions. As Einstein wished to emphasize the natural difference between space and time, he was obliged to search for a *fourth* coordinate which would be as different from the three conventional space coordinates as time itself was from space. Therefore, to present time, he employed what he called the *t*, or *time,* axis. This axis, however, is *purely imaginary.*

What, you ask, is an imaginary axis? Why even bother to consider something if it is only imaginary? Obviously this *t* axis is *not* only something we imagine, because if you will remember we learned earlier that our space axes do not actually exist either. We merely suppose or "imagine" them for our convenience in order to make space-distance measurements as promptly as we make measurements of purely physical bodies. (Here we are using the term "imaginary" in its mathematical, not its popular, sense.)

An imaginary axis is different from the palpable dimensions of real bodies; also it is basically different from the axes of a space coordinate. Furthermore, the *t* axis is not a real quantity, but is only a concept of which we have made an image in our minds. Scientists have found that this procedure is highly rewarding. To learn why, let's get acquainted with the quantities mathematicians call "imaginary" ones.

Consider the following illustration (Fig. 11). A host invites seven

Figure 11. The distinction between positive and negative quantities. The host does not really "have" the three borrowed chairs; he actually "has" minus three chairs.

guests to a party but has only four chairs. If he does not want three of his guests to sit on the floor, he must borrow the missing chairs.

The four chairs he positively possesses are positive quantities and may be marked by the positive or plus (+) sign. The three chairs he has borrowed, however, he does not possess; they are, therefore, for the host, negative or minus (−) quantities.

The minus sign means *No!* No, we do not really have the three borrowed chairs; we actually have minus three chairs. Likewise, we also have minus three dollars when we not only do not possess them but are indebted to someone for them; actually we "possess" three times less than a dollar.

All quantities or "numbers" in *arithmetics* have their value and may be presented as following one after the other on a line in strict order. This "line" is divided at its mid-point, which is then designated zero. Right of zero are positive numbers; left of it, negative numbers, like this:

87654321 0 12345678

− +

Think back a moment to our three-dimensional coordinate system. Isn't this line quite similar to the horizontal coordinate, or X axis, especially if we realize that the X axis may have, together with its positive side, a negative one too? As a matter of fact, the X axis is used in geometry for the same determination of values as the line of numbers in arithmetics.

When we work with the right-hand or positive numbers—found on the right-hand side of our line—we have little trouble manipulating them. All operations—addition, multiplication, even extraction of roots—go smoothly. Unfortunately, this is not always the case with the minus quantities on the left side of the line. They sometimes behave quite strangely. Take, for instance, −4. We know that the square root of +4 is +2 or −2, but can you extract the square root of −4? If you tried for an eternity you could never perform this seemingly simple operation. Is there no real number which would be the result of the square root of −4?

Perhaps some mathematical trick will help us. In mathematics, as it is well known, we can say the same thing in different ways. For example:

-4 is, in "other words," 4 *times* -1. Returning to our problem, we have:

$$\sqrt{-4} = \sqrt{4 \cdot (-1)}$$
$$\sqrt{-4} = 2 \cdot \sqrt{-1}$$

Now every high school student can extract the square root of $+4$ and get ± 2. Yet, as we see, the $\sqrt{-1}$ still remains. There is no getting rid of $\sqrt{-1}$!

Once again, let us resort to our Guided Tour appliances. Let's suppose that we are actually able to touch the line where all real numbers are located and attempt to find the rightful position of this elusive quantity $\sqrt{-1}$.

For the first time our equipment fails us! The quantity $\sqrt{-1}$ doesn't fit in anywhere and we must therefore assume that there is *no such quantity in reality.*

For centuries this mathematical paradox tantalized mathematicians all over the world. Finally Leonhard Euler, a Swiss mathematician, declared:

"The quantity $\sqrt{-1}$ does not exist at all in reality! It is not a real quantity, but an imaginary one!"

Subsequently, $\sqrt{-1}$ became known as i to distinguish *i*maginary quantities from known and unknown, yet real, algebraic quantities such as a, b, c, x, y, z and so on.

Suddenly, however, we seem to have many imaginary quantities, for we have just used the plural case. This is so because any real quantity multiplied by i becomes an imaginary quantity. For example, just as 5 times x is $5x$, so is 5 times i, $5i$.

Now, since there is no place for the i's among the real quantities on the horizontal X axis, let's place them, as the German mathematician Karl Friedrich Gauss suggested, *outside* of this line of numbers on a vertical axis. This he called the i axis because it was no more real than the i quantities themselves. This i axis later became Einstein's time-coordinate t.

It should be clearly understood that this vertical i (or t) axis has nothing to do with the *Y* or *Z* Cartesian coordinate axes marking height and depth distances in plane or space presentations. The *Y* axis, in fact, is vertical or perpendicular to the horizontal axis, but the imaginary vertical *i* axis is *entirely outside* the three-dimensional space-coordinate system.

If you still think that this imaginary axis may somehow exist somewhere in space, take a pencil and actually try to draw a vertical line on a sheet of paper. You will see that you cannot do this. All you can do is to depict its "image" in perspective.

It is likewise impossible to add a fourth coordinate to a normal three-dimensional space-coordinate system. There is simply no "room" for it. Only *some image* of a time coordinate may be put there—a set of clocks, for instance, which mark the time distances or their mathematical symbols.

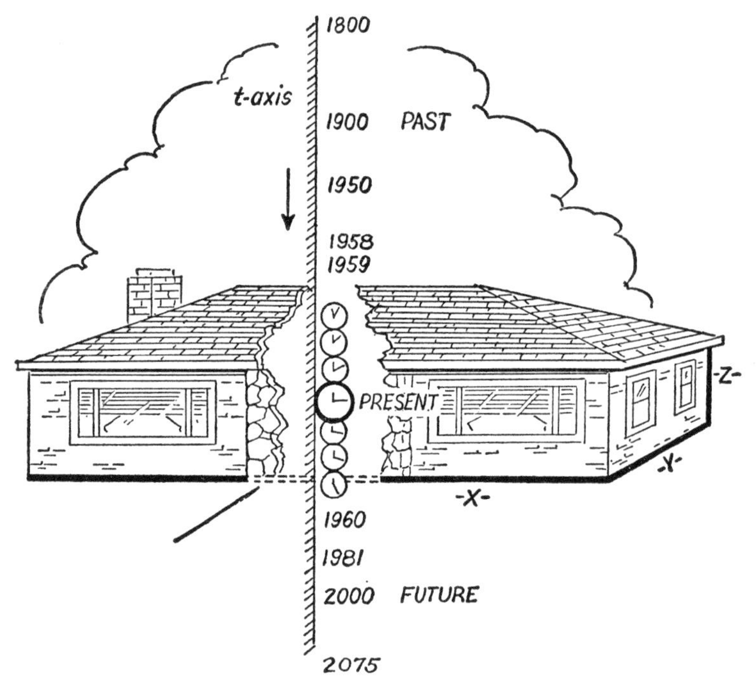

Figure 12. "Yesterday" cannot really be depicted in the "time house" except by Einstein's imaginary *t* axis.

Look at the house in Figure 12 and you will begin to see why Einstein chose to use this imaginary *t* axis to demonstrate that time—which is different in nature from space—nevertheless contracts like space itself under the influence of high velocities. Actually "yesterday" cannot *really* be depicted in the house, although yesterday was certainly there—just as "today," or, more exactly, the present moment, is there "now" for a short, finite time duration. If the house was built before the Civil War, then presumably at some time or other soldiers in Civil War uniforms walked through the house. Likewise, if the house stands 100 years hence, people of the future will move about in it. In both cases, there is no "real" way of representing these temporal events except by imaginary means. All we "see" now inside the house is the clock on the wall, ticking away an endless series of "present moments" from the "future" and turning them into "past's."

Yet, where *is* yesterday? Physically it is nonsense to ask this question, except to say that it is somewhere on the *t* axis. And, the *t* axis is imaginary.

As we see from the drawing, the clocks progress from minute to minute with comparative slowness inside the house. Outside the house on the *t* axis, however, the year 1900 does not seem very far in the past—nor does the year 2000 in the future. It takes little time at all, for example, to relive an event that happened ten years before by simply thinking of it, but it appears to take "forever" for a pot of coffee to percolate on the stove.

It is in this sense that we say in ordinary life that time is relative. We will learn a bit later what relativity of time means for the physicist.

We know that time, which we are incapable of perceiving with our senses, exists. The very reason why bodies, indeed space itself, have existence as we know it is that they exist in time. If they did not exist for a certain time they would only "exist" for a zero time duration; in other words, they would not exist at all.

Three-dimensional space thus has its existence and movement in the fourth dimension—time—without which it could have no being. Now space and time react together and in the same way at high velocities. There is no reason, therefore, physicists concluded, to distinguish between them in such systems.

"Space in itself and time in itself sink to mere shadows," asserted the German mathematician Minkowski, an early leader in relativistic dynamics. "Their union, however, is a definition of existence." Minkowski first stated this new concept in 1908; he called it *space-time.**

Yet how was this unification *actually* accomplished? How could Einstein combine space with time, hours with yards? Einstein accomplished this unusual task by unusual mathematical means.

We remember how the Pythagorean Theorem simplified the problem of our skindiver earlier. Einstein showed that this simplification is also possible when we combine the fourth dimension—or time interval—with the three spatial distances.

We cannot, however, combine a set of quantities and get a meaningful answer unless they are in terms of the same units of measurement. Time, therefore, has to be expressed in terms of the same units as space concepts, that is, in miles, yards, or feet—not in hours, minutes or seconds. We remember how the concept of velocity, which unites space and time elements, served as a bridge between them, and also how the tremendous velocity of light is the basis of the concept of the "light year" which is obtained by *multiplying* velocity by time. Similarly, a light mile, a light yard, or a light foot would be length *divided by* velocity. A light foot is the *time* necessary for light to travel the *distance* of one foot. With this very small time-quantity, about 0.000000001 of a second, Einstein was able to establish for how long a time duration a three-dimensional distance existed in space. Yet light feet are still time units, expressed in seconds, while space distances are expressed in ordinary feet or yards. To eliminate the difference between *a foot* and *a light foot,* Minkowski suggested turning the latter into imaginary light feet. How? By multiplication. We know that any real quantity turns into an imaginary quantity if multiplied by i (or $\sqrt{-1}$).

Einstein, when *generalizing* the Pythagorean Theorem so that it

---

* In German, *Zeitraum.*

also included time, stated that the entire four-dimensional spacetime interval is the square root of the sum of the three space distances raised to the second power *minus* the square of the time duration *times* the square of *c*. Or, in equation form:

$$\sqrt{X^2 + Y^2 + Z^2 - c^2t^2}$$

in which c is the constant velocity of light. Thus, the expression $-c^2t^2$ becomes not a squared unit of time, but length squared.

This is called the *generalization* of the Pythagorean Theorem. Might not such mathematics be a help to our skindiver if he were

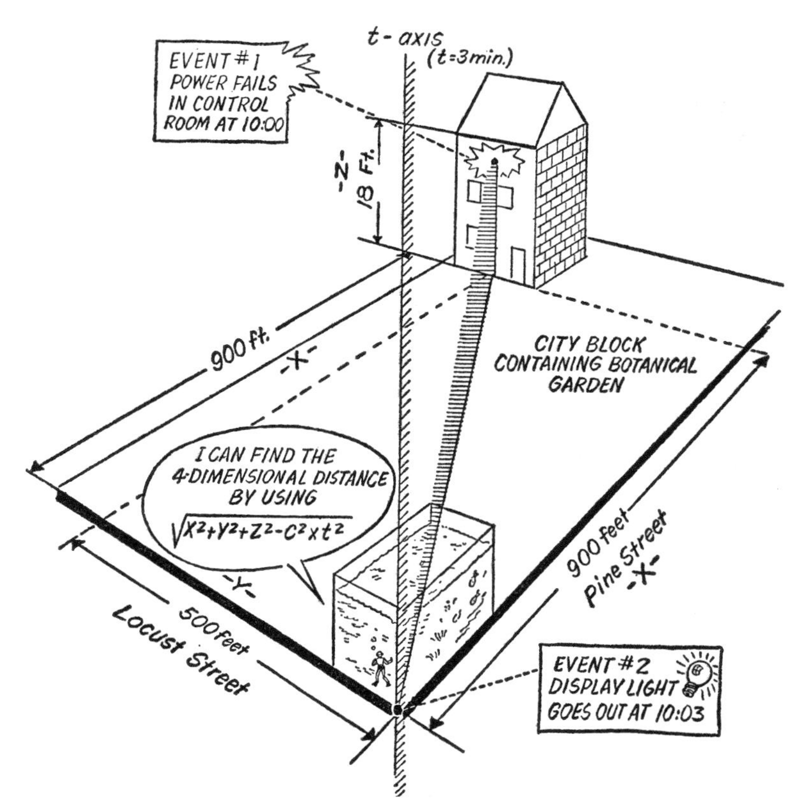

Figure 13. Skindiver finding the spacetime distance between two events by means of the generalized Pythagorean Theorem.

faced with a problem involving *time* as well as spatial distances?

Let us imagine once again that our skindiver is working in the large tank at the botanical gardens, tending his rare sea flowers (Fig. 13). Several yards away from the tank is a small power station. This station provides electricity for the botanical garden, which occupies an entire city block. As the skindiver is working, he happens to see a flash in the direction of the power station. The skindiver notes that the flash occurred precisely at 10:00. Three minutes later, at 10:03, one of the display lights in the nearest corner of the tank goes out.

Although the skindiver was under water at the time of the flash, he knows it must have occurred at a precise spot on the third floor of the power station, for that is where the transformer is which serves that part of his tank.

The skindiver decides that it would be an interesting exercise in relativity to calculate the entire four-dimensional interval between Event #1 (the failure of the power) and Event #2 (the extinguishing of the light). Since the latter event occurred at the corner of the tank (and also the city block occupied by the botanical gardens at Locust and Pine Streets), he sets up his *X*, *Y*, and *Z* coordinates there. Then he carefully measures along them to get his spatial values. On the *X* axis (Pine St.) he finds the distance between Events #1 and #2 to be 900 feet. On the *Y* axis (Locust St.) he gets 500 feet. On the *Z* axis (height of the event from zero coordinate to the third floor transformer) he gets 18 feet. The value for the *t* axis, of course, he knows to be 3 minutes (or 180 seconds). The four-dimensional spacetime distance between the two events which he wishes to find he calls *M*.

Knowing the space distances to be 900, 500 and 18 feet respectively, the skindiver substitutes them in Einstein's generalized Pythagorean Theorem:

$$\sqrt{x^2 + y^2 + z^2 - c^2 \cdot t^2} \text{ and gets}$$

$$\sqrt{(900)^2 + (500)^2 + (18)^2 - c^2 \cdot t^2} = M$$

He easily solves the first part of his equation, 900^2 being 810,000; 500^2 being 250,000; and 18^2 being 324, and their sum total equaling 1,060,324. Thus,

$$\sqrt{1{,}060{,}324 - c^2 \cdot t^2} = M$$

Since the square of an imaginary number is negative the skindiver hopes that by keeping the minus sign (−) before the time interval of 3 minutes expressed in light feet he can obtain imaginary light feet, thus defining the entire four-dimensional distance as the square root of the sum of the squares of all four coordinate distances.

Then he realizes that he cannot subtract light feet from feet and that, to solve his problem, he must actually express all his data in the same unit. In other words $c \cdot t$ must be in units of length. For his problem, $c = 10^9$ feet/sec; $t = 180$ seconds. So that $ct = 180 \times 10^9$ (or 180,000,000,000 feet). Thus the equation becomes:

$$\sqrt{1{,}060{,}324 - (180{,}000{,}000{,}000)^2} = M$$

But even if our skindiver is acquainted with this much of mathematical physics it would be ridiculous to subtract 1,060,325 from such a gigantic number.

It would be better to write the last equation as approximately

$$180{,}000{,}000{,}000\sqrt{-1}\text{ ft.}$$

The skindiver's problem shows how complex—and how absurd—the data obtained by the generalization of the Pythagorean Theorem can be when applied to events in daily life. The figures, however, would be more reasonable if both events had happened on two swiftly moving spaceships in outer space where spatial distances would have been greater. Actually, in cases where systems have velocities approximating that of light, the four-dimensional coordinate is a more suitable tool. Yet in such systems alterations in space and time must be considered.

Lorentz's transformation equations give an indication of the contraction of dimensions in such high-velocity systems, but not until Einstein generalized these equations and introduced time as a variable quantity could scientists tell by which factor they must adjust space and time devices in order to get valid data in any two systems moving relative to each other.

In our next chapter, we shall see how Einstein used these equations to prove that two observers, moving relative to each other, can determine light's velocity to be constant for both of them, provided they adjust their spacetime devices accordingly.

CHAPTER NINE

TWO BOYS ON A CLOUD, AND A GREEK LETTER

SPACETIME ADJUSTMENT

The two observers Einstein used as examples in his writings, together with their systems, were similar to and in a way also different from ours in the slow balloon and fast spaceship.

They were similar inasmuch as they moved relative to one another; their relative motion had constant velocity and thus their speed and direction remained uniform and straight. Yet Einstein's observers and their systems were different from ours in one significant way. Our balloon and spaceship were supposed to be discontinuous material bodies, as vehicles of course are. Einstein, however, did not postulate such reference systems. Because he wanted to present a new dynamics, his only concern was with the *motion* of these systems. Thus, he postulated them in empty space and considered them as being without material characteristics.

Since motion in the realm of high velocities is not performed by discontinuous steps, but is uninterrupted and continuous, Einstein also represented it by continuous systems. This he achieved by using differential equations.

Previously, we encountered continuously moving systems in Faraday's electromagnetic field and also the differential equations used by Maxwell to present them. These equations were also familiar to the German physicist Woldemar Voigt, who with them determined mechanical vibratory motions. Later Lorentz based on them his *transformation equations,* which showed how the lengths of bodies contract in the direction of their motion. Lorentz, however, could not avoid accepting the ether concept and stated that this stationary frame of reference possessed "true" time, while any moving system had an "artificial" time. When Einstein rejected the ether hypothesis, he declared that *any* system which moves relative to another has equal right in claiming its time to be the "true" one.

Time, stated Einstein, is not measurable in itself. We create the concept of time simply to arrange or order series of events. Like any other measuring unit, time serves purely to make comparisons possible. "Early" and "late," for example, are man-made definitions. They cannot be applied, however, unless we know relative *to what* we are applying them. This is what physicists understand by the *relativity of time.*

In studying the tiny band of visible colors in the immense ocean of invisible radiations, we saw how limited our human sight actually is. These limits, in fact, form the walls of that "human prison" visualized by Plato. All we know and possess of the world—sweetness and warmth, light and motion—exist for us only if they register on our senses. Likewise, Einstein persuaded us that time, like space, is also mere opinion—as are all concepts we form from the few phenomena we are able to recognize. This subjective viewpoint is the key to the solution which Einstein found in his coordinates and equations.

The efficacy of Einstein's No. 1 coordinate with X, Y, and Z space axes, and his No. 2 coordinate with X', Y', Z' axes is thus expanded by t and t' time axes. When translated into the language of equations, the ordinary differential calculus had to be "widened" accordingly. The result was the *tensor* calculus developed by Riemann, which requires more than three dimensions for its functions.

Now we shall attempt to translate the No. 1 coordinate: $X^2 + Y^2 + 2^2 - (c^2 \cdot t^2)$, and the No. 2 coordinate: $X'^2 + Y'^2 + 2'^2 - (c^2 \cdot t'^2)$, into more understandable terms by an illustration.

We shall not represent these systems by balloons or spaceships this time, for it is difficult to visualize how these separate and distinct vehicles would "transform" when their length and time both shrink. We all know that this happens in high-velocity systems, yet even high velocity cannot actually cut out a piece of space and time as a knife does a slice from a loaf of bread. This transformation occurs *con-*

tinuously and, therefore, we must present it by continuous systems. Clouds, say, whose limits are seldom clear-cut when they are in motion, would be excellent for our purpose.

Let us say, therefore, that System No. 1 is a big cloud; on it sits a fat boy who is an observer (Fig. 14). The fat boy's cloud moves

Figure 14. How two observers moving relative to each other can determine light's velocity (c) to be the same for both.

relative to System No. 2, which is a small cloud. This cloud is much swifter and on it sits a thin boy who is also an observer. Naturally both boys have been provided with a suit of our special equipment before starting out. Let us also suppose that both boys on their respective clouds are moving along Einstein's t axis somewhere in outer space—or, if you like, through a gigantic "Time Sky."

The boys' assignment is to determine whether c, the velocity of light, is constant and the same for both of them; and, if it is not, to find out what they can do to adjust their systems to make it so. Two light rays then arrive from the sun and the boys attempt to measure their velocity. Being familiar with pre-Einsteinian dynamics, they suppose that it is enough simply to adjust their spatial measuring devices to account for the spatial alterations caused by the difference of their velocities.

The boys, however, fail to obtain the same results. Suddenly one of them remembers that a certain Doctor Einstein has provided him with a prescription to remedy the situation. Doctor Einstein's prescription says that not only length shrinks at high velocities but also that time slows down; length *and* time, he says, must be corrected by using a "formula" called by our boys simply β (*Beta,* a Greek letter) which is an abbreviation for a complex multiplier.

When the boys adjust their space *and* time devices, according to this formula, and again measure the velocity of light in their respective clouds they obtain identical results of 186,000 mi/sec, even though the velocities of their systems remain different.

This factor β shows the *ratio of alterations* which spatial and temporal dimensions suffer when the velocities of their systems approach that of light. In other words this multiplier is a synchronizer of time *and* space transformations occurring in nature when high velocities are involved.

Once again we see that the velocity of a moving system, regardless of how high this velocity may be, is not added to the velocity of light. Although it may contradict all common sense, the sum of two such velocities is never more than the individual velocity of light.

Now, just for the fun of it, let us suppose that our fat boy falls asleep on his cloud. He has been eating more candy than is good for him and he has a nightmare. He dreams that a mysterious force suddenly begins accelerating Cloud No. 1. This velocity accelerates until it reaches and then surpasses the velocity of light. The boy dreams that he and his cloud shrink more and more, that time slows down until it stops and that he, together with his cloud, disappear into the infinite. At this point our boy wakes with a scream.

By now, it is obvious to us that the fat boy's experience could only *be* a dream, for we have learned that no moving system in our material world can attain, let alone surpass, the velocity of light. This constant velocity seems to be the supreme limit possible in nature.

Yet, if we take physicists' word for this, how is it possible that the c in Einstein's equations can be squared—that is, multiplied by itself to produce a tremendous quantity? Simply because all other quantities in the equation are also raised to the second power. And in mathematics, whatever we do to one factor in an equation we must also do to the others. But does nature itself follow this formula? How does the constant velocity of light act in reality when raised to the second power instead of merely appearing as a number in an abstract formula?

The next three chapters will try to answer these and other questions.

CHAPTER △ TEN

ENERGY INTO MASS—AND VICE VERSA: $E = mc^2$

CONSERVATION OF MASS & ENERGY

When physicists attempted to accelerate the speed of an emitted particle so that it approached the velocity of light, they eventually reached a point where the particle's speed could not be increased beyond that limit. Now, what became of the "extra" energy which supposedly might have—but actually did not—accelerate the particle further?

The answer was found when such accelerated particles were weighed after the experiment and found to have become heavier! In other words, their mass had increased—in some cases, several hundred times.

When the term "mass" is used we tend to think of it as the quantity of matter which a certain body possesses. For the physicist, however, mass is not identical with material volume. For him, mass is matter's *attitude toward* the force which accelerates it. Thus the mass of a material body marks its proportionate relationship to the accelerating force.

The energy which the particles could not use to further accelerate their speed had *increased* the weight of the particles. Energy had increased mass. *Energy, in fact, had been transformed into matter!*

To demonstrate this, let us make an experiment of our own. Suppose we board a transparent train which can move with the speed of light (Fig. 15). Not entirely convinced that the train can't go faster, we bring aboard an additional supply of non-material high-energy fuel in a suitcase. We hand the suitcase over to the engineer with instructions to use it when the speed of 186,000 mi/sec has been attained in order to accelerate the train's velocity further. Smiling, the engineer promises to try. Pretty soon, however, we notice that the train is moving with the speed of light, yet has not exceeded it. When we complain to the engineer, he hands us

Figure 15. Energy is transformed into matter under tremendous velocities, and vice versa. Again the spacemen find they cannot exceed the velocity of light. Had the experiment been real, both men would have been transformed into the energy state.

back what we gave him. Instead of being the suitcase, however, it is now a very tiny, heavy package. Obviously our light-train, being unable to use this additional energy, stored it away in the form of matter.

This energy fuel was not "lost," but simply changed its *state* under the tremendous velocity. This illustrates the linking of two important laws of physics by the Theory of Relativity—the Laws of Conservation of Energy and of Matter—which state that neither *matter nor energy can be created or destroyed.* Energy and matter cannot simply "disappear" in nature; neither can "something" be created out of nothing.

Now if energy can be transformed into matter, it is logical to assume that matter may also become energy. Scientists might have discovered this long ago had they had our light-train at their disposal to examine such transformations. However, it was not until Einstein himself stated that energy and matter were the one and the same "thing" that this basic law of nature was recognized.

When he showed the relationship between the two in his celebrated equation $E = mc^2$, he demonstrated how from a very tiny particle of matter tremendous energy can be released in the ratio of the square of the velocity of light. Not energy separately or mass separately are constant, but the sum total of energy *and* mass (multiplied by c^2) is constant and cannot increase or decrease. Thus the Theory of Relativity states that there is a fundamental equivalence between mass and energy, based on the relationship of mass and speed.

Matter and energy are thus interchangeable. If matter moves with a velocity approximating that of light it becomes energy; if energy is sufficiently slowed down we call it matter.

Einstein resolved the conflict of matter and energy by fusing together the opposed concepts of space and time. Again and again, the study of matter and the observation of radiant energies yielded brilliant proofs of his abstract theories.

Let's first examine those offered by radiations, and secondly, those found in matter. During our next chapter we may, for the time being, put away our suits of special equipment. They will not be necessary in comprehending how man discovered radiant energy he could not see, and how he split the very center of the atom, transforming matter into energy.

CHAPTER ELEVEN

VISIBLE AND INVISIBLE RADIATION

SPECTRAL ANALYSIS

RELATIVISTIC "RED SHIFT" & "DOPPLER EFFECT"

RADIOACTIVITY—α, β, γ RAYS

Wavelike electromagnetic radiations, as we saw in a previous chapter, were discovered experimentally following Maxwell's theoretical conclusions. These phenomena had always existed in nature. X-rays, for example, had always been able to penetrate our bodies, yet no one knew of their existence until Wilhelm Roentgen, a German physicist, discovered them in 1895. Heretofore, all that man had been able to see of the range of electromagnetic radiations was the band of colors we know as the visible spectrum.

It was Newton who first produced such a "spectrum." He made a tiny hole in a window shade allowing a small beam of sunlight to enter his room. He refracted this beam through a simple prism and then "admired on the opposite wall all the colors of the rainbow from violet to red." Newton thus demonstrated that white light is made up of all known colors and that there is no break between these colors.

Today, however, scientists can improve on the naked eye by using a *spectroscope,* an instrument which separates colors produced by light. If we use this instrument to take a sample of the sun's light, we immediately notice that the *spectrogram* we receive is not a continuous one but is crossed by dark lines. Joseph von Fraunhofer, a German physicist, first observed these "lines" at the beginning of the last century. The so-called *Fraunhofer lines* bear his name.

Why these dark lines existed was found out only later by another German, Gustav Kirchhoff. He demonstrated that there are intensely hot gases in the sun which absorb light, thus causing dark lines between the colors. By the absence of certain colors and their replacement by dark lines in certain positions, we know that thus-and-such an element is therefore present in the sun. One after the other, these dark-line-causing gases were discovered and identified with their terrestrial equivalents—with the exception of one which absorbed a particularly vivid shade. From this physicists concluded that there must be a gas in the sun which is not present on the earth and called it Helium (from *Helios,* "sun" in Greek). A quarter of a century later, however, a small amount of Helium was actually discovered on our globe, thus confirming the Fraunhofer-Kirchhoff theory.

How did Kirchhoff know that these gases absorb light? Simply because he observed that they also *emit* light. And the wavelength of the emitted light must be the same as the wavelength of the absorbed light!

Important discoveries in radiations beyond the visible spectrum were also made by Sir William Hershel, the English astronomer, who observed radiations whose wavelengths were 7½ times longer than the wavelengths of visible radiations. Since they were located beyond the red end of the visible spectrum, they were called *infrared* waves, and were identified with heat. Later, as we know, Hertz discovered radio waves with even longer wavelengths.

When we study visible and invisible radiations we are actually performing *spectral analysis.* This method of observation indicates wavelengths which are marked by λ (*lambda,* a Greek letter). These are measured in microns, or Angstrom Units, and are partially spatial concepts.

Spectral analysis also determines frequencies of various wavelengths; that is, the number of vibrations or oscillations which the waves perform in a given unit of time. Frequency, being compounded from wavelength and light-velocity, is thus partially a time concept. Therefore spectroscopic research may well be called a "spacetime measuring system." We shall presently see how it aided atomic research from the very beginning.

If we search for actual proof of Einstein's theories, we find that too in spectral analyses. Spectroscopy shows that light arriving from a distant star differs from light emanating from an earthly light-source because its spectrum is slightly shifted toward the red or longer wavelengths.

This "relativistic" red shift must not be confused with the so-called *Doppler effect,* which means simply that to an observer approaching the source of any wave motion, sound or radiation, the frequency appears greater than to an observer moving away. Thus light emitted by a receding body appears to be of lower frequency (more red) than if the source and observer did not move relatively to each other.

Yet the Einsteinian red shift, caused by the relativistic time alteration, is also based on the fact that all radiation is precisely related to the amount of energy released at its source. Since each element has its own structure, a particular element exhibits a unique group of spectral colors. Colors of each type of radiation occurring, for example, on a distant star can thus be compared with the colors of the same type of radiation occurring on earth. Frequencies (that is, *time per vibration*) on the distant star being retarded (as predicted by the Theory of Special Relativity), light is shifted toward the red or longer wavelengths.

Moving to the right side of the spectrum, beyond the visible violet light, we find ultraviolet rays whose wavelengths are extremely short. Ultraviolet rays were first "seen," that is, photographed, by Henri Becquerel in the last quarter of the past century. This French physicist accidentally left a piece of a then little-known uranium ore called "pitchblende" on top of a closed box of sensitive photographic plates in a drawer. When he later developed this plate he discovered in one corner a dark spot which had taken the shape of the mineral.

Becquerel knew that the plate had been very carefully wrapped in heavy black paper which no normal light could have penetrated.

He concluded that something in this mineral must have acted as light does, only in a much more efficient way. He found that this something was a powerful radiation which uranium emits and which is even more penetrating than X-rays. Uranium, he stated, was a *radioactive* substance. Later a favorite pupil of Becquerel's, Marie Curie, was to carry out her world-famed work in this field.

This young Polish-born chemist found that there were other minerals which behaved as uranium did, some with even greater intensities. When Madame Curie and her husband eventually discovered the radioactive element which is present in all these radioactive minerals they called it *radium*. Subsequently, radioactivity itself was defined as the property of an element which causes that element to emit particles or radiations.

Other scientists now turned their attention to this phenomenon. Ernest Rutherford, the English physicist, in experimenting with these radiations, passed them through an electromagnetic field and found that they separated into three different kinds of radiations. He called them after Greek letters: *alpha* (α), *beta* (β) and *gamma* (γ) rays. These turned out to be very different from one another. Alpha rays were charged with positive (+) electricity; beta rays were charged with negative (–) electricity and traveled with a velocity close to that of light. Gamma rays had *no* electrical charge and were similar to X-rays, although they possessed much shorter wavelengths.

Rutherford thus interpreted the radioactivity of so-called "heavy" elements to be actually a spontaneous *transformation* of unstable chemical elements into one another.

The complete electromagnetic spectrum of visible *and* invisible radiations looks something like this (if we add the cosmic rays—those with very short wavelengths which arrive from outer space):

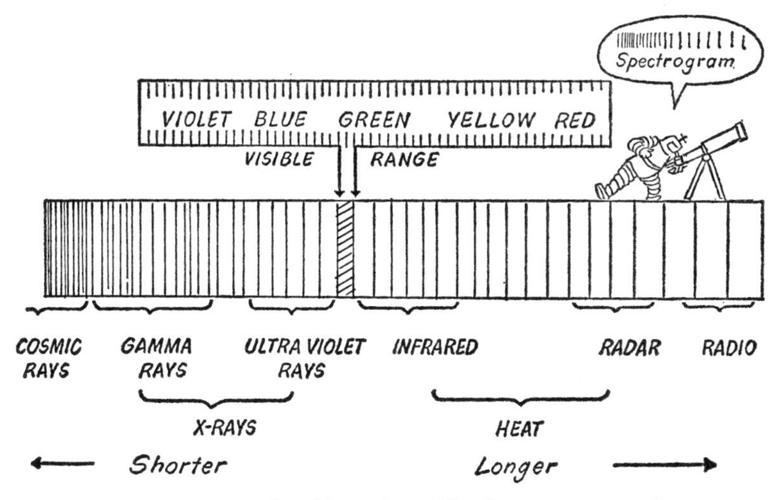

Figure 16. Spectrum of visible and invisible electromagnetic radiation.

With the making of these important discoveries, the work which had begun with Becquerel and the Curies resulted in fulfillment of the dream of Medieval alchemists who had spent lifetimes in trying to transmute base metals into gold. The "gold" in this case, however, was to be a far more valuable contribution to the world than mere precious yellow metal. It was to lead to the fabulous source of power which we know as atomic energy.

CHAPTER △ TWELVE

"THE ITALIAN NAVIGATOR HAS LANDED"

ELEMENTS & ATOMS

THE PERIODIC TABLE

THE "EMPTY" ATOM

ATOMIC FISSION

Are you certain you know what an *element* is? Put in its simplest terms, it is the basic ingredient of something. Ancient Greek philosophers believed that water, air, stone and fire were the basic elements of nature—substances which we know today are not elementary at all.

One of these ancients, Leucippus, noticed how frozen water becomes ice, and how thawing ice becomes water again, and stated that substances possess some elementary characteristics which they can never lose. From this notion of one fundamental substance, which Leucippus called *a-tom* (something indivisible), the concept of *atomism,* or *unity of matter,* was conceived.

A century ago a British physicist named Prout came forward with a curious idea. He stated that all elements were built from a single primary element and that this primary element was *hydrogen,* the lightest of all elements. Later discoveries caused Prout's hypothesis to be rejected; subsequently, however, his theory was found to be justified.

Of the approximately 100 known chemical elements, each is built of these indestructible atoms. Every element is composed of like atoms with identical characteristics which are unlike the atoms of any other element. All hydrogen atoms, for example, are alike and are likewise different from oxygen atoms, as well as the atoms of all other elements.

Elements are able to form *compounds,* that is, more complex substances. Hydrogen, for instance, combines with oxygen to form water, which is a chemical compound. There are always two hydrogen atoms for every one of oxygen in water. It was John Dalton who stated this relationship in his *law of constant proportions:* the amounts of different chemical elements needed to form a definite chemical compound always stand in a certain given ratio.

Since each element possesses a measurable weight, scientists soon found that they could be arranged and referred to in a definite manner by their increasing atomic weight. Mendelejev, a Russian chemist, demonstrated that the regularity of their arrangement is a *periodic* one. In 1869 he compiled a *periodic table* in which he determined the exact place for each known element, leaving empty places for elements that he claimed existed but which were not yet discovered. Exactly as he predicted, all of these elements were later found.

The following is a simplified periodic table showing how the pattern works:

Chemical Property	First Period	Second Period	Third Period
	Hydrogen		
Alkaloid		Lithium	Sodium
Intermediary	———	Nitrogen Oxygen	Aluminum Silicon
Acidifier	———	Fluorine	Chlorine
"Noble" or rare gas	Helium	Neon	Argon

. . . and so on until the periodic table ends with the heaviest elements like uranium. Among them are the "unstable" elements which disintegrate spontaneously in nature; these are the radioactive elements such as radium.

The periodic system begins with the lightest element, hydrogen—the No. 1 element—and proceeds with heavier and heavier elements as their atomic weights increase. The "rare" or "noble gases" are so-called because they do not mingle or "prefer" to form compounds. These "noble gases," such as helium, neon, argon, actually mark the endings of the various periods. The pattern is always the same: a period begins with an alkaloid such as lithium or sodium and proceeds toward an acidifier such as fluorine or chlorine, then terminates with a "noble" gas. Between are intermediary elements such as nitrogen or silicon.

The smallest particle of a substance, either an element or a compound which still possesses the properties of that substance, is called a *molecule*. The building stones of *elements* are known to be *atoms*.

All atoms belonging to the same element have identical chemical properties, yet their mass may be different. Atoms having the same properties and thus the same *atomic number* but possessing different masses are called *isotopes*.

Atoms were, for a long time, considered to be the smallest indivisible parts of matter. The discovery of the electron changed this belief.

We recognize electricity as the continuous flow of charges along a conductor. Electricity, we say today, consists of electrons in such a flow. That electricity could be divided into discrete units first occurred to Faraday, discoverer of the continuous motion of electromagnetic forces, when studying the phenomenon of electrolysis. The electrolytic process works like this: acid is dissolved in water; when a current is passed through the solution the water decomposes into its elements, hydrogen and oxygen. Faraday found that in a certain length of time, a specified amount of current *always* deposits the same amount of these elements. In other words, the amount of an element liberated from its compound is proportional to the quantity of electricity passing through the solution.

Analysis of these elements proved that they were electrically charged—the hydrogen atoms positively, the oxygen atoms negatively. These electrically charged atoms in fluids were called *ions*.

Faraday also found that the electric charge of these ions is *always* equal to a certain amount of electricity or a multiple of that amount. This amount of electricity was equal to the charge of an ionized hydrogen atom and *appeared to be the elementary unit of electricity.*

This discovery had several important consequences. It meant first that hydrogen might indeed be the primary element in nature—the master building stone of them all, as Prout had supposed earlier. It meant also that the bond between elements in a compound is electric in nature. But most important was the recognition that these observed amounts of electricity were distinct units of definite size.

Then another Englishman, J. J. Thomson, noticed that when an electric current was passed through a rarefied gas, the positive ions behaved exactly as in liquids—but with one important exception. Whereas the positive ions were similar to those in the electrolysis of liquids, the mass of the negative ions was much, much smaller than that of any atom. It began to look as if an electric charge could actually be liberated from the mass in which it was previously thought to be imprisoned. This free charge then was called an *electron.* When Robert A. Millikan, an American scientist, measured an electron he found that it has exactly the same charge as the entire negatively charged ion without leaving its mass.

The fact that an electron could be detached from the mass of the atom was the first sign that the atom is not an indivisible unit, but itself is composed of positively and negatively charged parts.

Now if the electron was the smallest unit of electricity—and since electricity was energy—could not all radiant energies consist of small discontinuous units? The answer to this question lay in Planck's famous Quantum Theory, a theory which ranked in importance with Einstein's Relativity. We shall be getting acquainted with it a little later on.

At this stage of scientific development, however, both scientists and laymen were more concerned with a less theoretical—and more exciting—possibility. This was the question of splitting the atom in order to tap the tremendous energy locked within it.

Thus atomic research began. First, Thomson constructed a model of the atom in which he presented the negative electron as being indeed imprisoned in a compact, positively charged mass (Fig. 17). Lord Rutherford, however, doubted this. He undertook to decompose the astonishingly tough nucleus of the atom by using the very rays he had discovered in analyzing radioactivity. In unsuccessfully trying to "bombard" an atom with these powerful rays, he concluded that the atom cannot be as tightly-knit a unit as Thomson supposed, because the powerful stream of high-energy particles which he aimed at the atom would have hit *something.* Time and again, however, Rutherford's rays had failed to collide with *anything* inside the atom.

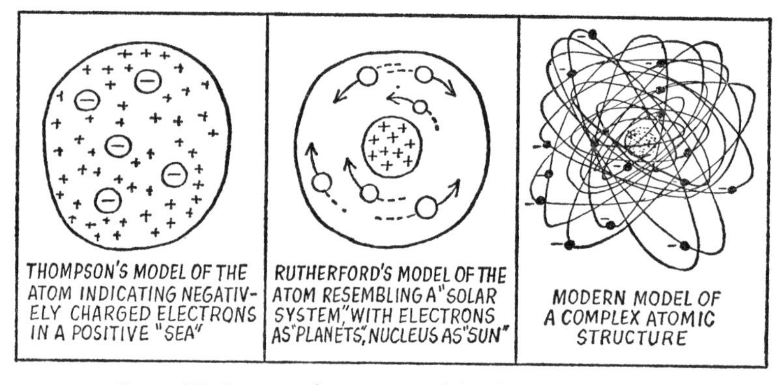

Figure 17. Some evolutionary models of atomic structure.

He was forced to conclude therefore that the atom, far from being a compact, motionless and static substance, is almost *empty* inside! He further stated that the inside of an atom is very much like a solar system with a positively charged center and negatively charged electrons orbiting around it, like planets around the sun.

To better understand just what Rutherford was up against, let us make brief use of our Guided Tour equipment. We board a spaceship which takes us a considerable distance outside our own solar system (Fig. 18). With us, we have a .22 rifle. We then stop the spaceship and see, very far away, the tiny speck which is the sun with its planets revolving about it. Then we begin firing bullets at the solar system in an attempt to hit something inside it. Indeed, we could fire our rifle for a whole year and we would be extremely lucky if we hit anything at all—even an asteroid. It was in this sense that Rutherford concluded that an atom is practically "empty."

As most of its mass was in its center, it was clear that, to split the atom, Rutherford had to bombard the atomic nucleus itself,

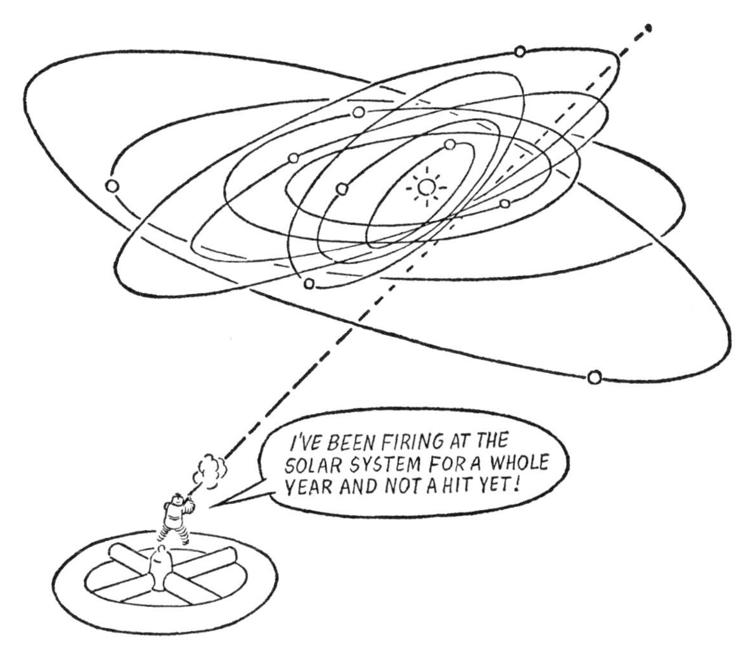

Figure 18. The atom, like our solar system, is almost empty inside.

for the electrons in the outer rings were exceedingly poor targets. In directing his particles at the nucleus, Rutherford was able to observe them with the help of Wilson's so-called "cloud-chamber."

This device is based on the fact that when hot humid air is cooled, drops of water are formed which, together with dust, produce fog. A similar situation existed in Wilson's cloud-chamber because the air there was "ionized" (electrically charged) by the introduction of charged particles. The ions, collecting on the drops of water, clearly showed the path the particles took.

This "line of fog" faithfully tracked Rutherford's alpha particles as they bombarded atoms of nitrogen gas in the chamber. When an alpha particle finally struck an atomic nucleus, two new particles appeared and the presence of hydrogen and oxygen was noticeable. Neither of those elements had been present before! With the conversion of nitrogen atoms into hydrogen and oxygen atoms, the first man-made transformation of elements in history was accomplished!

We know today that the atom consists, roughly speaking, of a positively charged nucleus, about which negatively charged electrons rotate in various orbits. The atom as a whole is normally neutral, that is, electrically balanced. The number of electrons may well indicate the atomic number of an element because the charge of any element expressed in elementary units is the same as its number on the periodic table. As we saw, hydrogen is No. 1 and possesses one electron; helium is No. 2 and possesses two electrons, and so on.

Further analyses of the nucleus showed that it consisted of positively charged particles called *protons,* and also particles with no charge at all called *neutrons*. It was subsequently demonstrated that the number of electrons in a neutral atom was the same as the number of protons in the nucleus.

Now, if an atomic nucleus is split, part of its mass is transformed into energy. Precisely this is the secret of the atom bomb.

This transformation follows Einstein's now-famous formula: $E = mc^2$. It was Rutherford who first confirmed it experimentally. How?

In another atom-splitting experiment, he bombarded a very light metal called lithium with the nuclei of hydrogen atoms. The result produced helium. When he measured the nuclei of this newly obtained element and compounded its energies, he found that the total energy of the helium nucleus was greater than the energy of the hydrogen nucleus and equivalent to the mass which had disappeared during the transformation. The ratio of the transformation of this mass into energy was exactly the amount predicted years before by Einstein's formula $E = mc^2$, where E means energy, m means mass and c^2 is the square of the velocity of light. When we consider what a tremendous quantity this latter figure represents, we see why such a tiny particle of material is capable of releasing such terrific energy.

Considering that Einstein presented his mass-into-energy formula as early as 1904, and Rutherford confirmed it by experimentation in 1919, why was the large-scale production of atomic energy not accomplished until as late as 1945?

Simply because the energy required to split the atom was considerably greater than the energy which resulted. Another reason was that once an atomic reaction was started no one knew at first how to control it.

Controlled production of atomic energy was only achieved when Otto Hahn, Lise Meitner and their co-workers succeeded in splitting an atom of uranium by neutron bombardment. Such particles, as we have seen, are neutral and without charge; hence, they are not affected by the various charges present in their target.

The energy released by the uranium was considerably greater than that of previous attempts at atom-splitting. And, among the particles produced, neutrons again appeared. Since neutrons started the reaction in the first place, it was hoped that these newly produced neutrons would in turn produce further explosions. The neutrons thus emitted by one single atom could go on to split many other atoms. This is known as a *chain reaction* and the splitting of the atom in this manner is called *atomic fission.*

This, however, was not the end of the story. You remember that one element may have a number of different isotopes. Now, only one isotope of uranium is fissionable, U^{235}. In U^{238}, some fission occurs but it is negligible under most circumstances. Besides, U^{238} absorbs the bombarding neutrons. After this absorption, however, U^{238} is transformed into another isotope, U^{239}, which is unstable and, in turn, forms a new element called neptunium. Likewise unstable, neptunium then forms yet another element known as plutonium. When bombarded with neutrons, plutonium explodes and produces the new neutrons required for a successful chain reaction.

Not all mass can be used to produce the chain reaction. The mass which is just right for this purpose was called *critical mass* and was determined to be less than 20 pounds, by Werner Heisenberg, one of the most outstanding living German scientists. Less than 20 pounds is not enough; more is too much and causes an almost uncontrollable explosion.

In the first large-scale atomic chain reaction, the controlling, or slowing down of the explosion, was accomplished in a basement of the University of Chicago. This was done by means of an *atomic pile* in which thick graphite bricks carefully controlled the fission of the atoms of the natural uranium they enclosed. This was the ultimate achievement of Enrico Fermi, an Italian-born scientist, and his co-workers. To mark this event there is a plaque at the University which reads:

ON DECEMBER 2, 1942, MAN ACHIEVED HERE THE FIRST SELF-SUSTAINING CHAIN REACTION AND THEREBY INITIATED THE CONTROLLED RELEASE OF NUCLEAR ENERGY.

Since this occurred during World War II, great secrecy was maintained for security reasons. When it became clear that their efforts were successful, the following cryptic wire was sent to Washington:

THE ITALIAN NAVIGATOR HAS LANDED.
THE NATIVES ARE FRIENDLY.

. . . which meant to those working on the famed Manhattan Project: "The Fermi-pile works successfully. Nuclear chain reaction is achieved."

Today the secret of the atomic bomb is a secret no longer. Yet the regular production of atomic energy still must be greatly perfected before it becomes in fact what it is in theory—mankind's cheapest and most efficient source of power.

CHAPTER △ THIRTEEN

GENERAL RELATIVITY

SPACETIME CONTINUUM

"WORLD LINES"

GEODESICS AND A TRAINED BEE

Einstein's principle of Special Relativity is based upon the ideal concept of pure motion proceeding at constant, never-varying velocities in perfectly straight lines through empty space.

However, no absolutely empty space exists in our world, and motion, in reality, is neither perfectly straight-lined nor does it possess constant speed. When Einstein generalized his theory for all types of motion, he had to take matter into consideration. This is the chief difference between Special Relativity and General Relativity. On the one hand, material phenomena can influence motion; on the other, a state of motion may change the aspects of matter. Therefore, anyone who searches for a true picture of our world faces their interaction. When these new dynamics left the abstract utopia of Special Relativity and stepped into the real world of General Relativity they had to cope with this reciprocal action.

We have seen how to find the spacetime of two events with the help of a four-dimensional coordinate system. We also saw how clumsy these coordinates are for skindivers or anyone else to use in real life. When someone in daily life wants to locate something exactly and also include that something's time datum, he simply employs a *graph*. A graph is itself a coordinate system with horizontal and vertical axes, and it is much handier to use.

The propagation of light, for instance, can also be described by a one-dimensional or linear graph. A one-dimensional graph consists of a one-dimensional coordinate. Length alone is enough to determine the path of light from one star to another. As this motion is continuous, the graph may be called a *one-dimensional continuum,* which is also continuous, as its name implies, and in which only one function exists.

This system is not sufficient, however, for a nurse who must determine the changing temperature of a patient at different hours during the day. Why? Because she must register *two* sets of data on her graph. She marks degrees of temperature on one axis and hours on the other. On this two-dimensional "plane" coordinate system the nurse then joins the successive readings she has taken with a line which she calls the patient's "fever curve." This curve, showing variations of temperature during the day, unites two *variables*—fever and time—both of which flow continuously. Such a system is called a *two-dimensional continuum.*

Now if a rocket expert is observing a ballistic missile in flight and wishes to know how high, how distant, and how much to the left of him the missile is, he is dealing with the three-spatial functions of our world—length, width and height—or a *three-dimensional continuum.*

If, however, the rocket expert wishes to know how the position of the missile changes during a certain time, he needs a four-dimensional graph. The motion of the missile through air-space, like the motion of any material object, is a *four-dimensional event.* But, if the flight of the missile, or any fast-moving material particle, is considered as a whole, it cannot be divided up into "parts" or individual events. Just as the individual frames of a motion picture film present the continuous story sequence of the movie when set in motion by a projector, so the entire path followed by a moving particle presents the continuous story of this particle. This path is traced by the curve uniting the particle's three spatial data and its single time datum. The four functions of a four-dimensional spacetime being continuous, such a system is referred to as a *four-dimensional continuum.*

Our entire world may be described as a four-dimensional continuum where space and time dimensions are interwoven. The functions of this continuum are variable quantities, just as space and time vary with different observers. We have seen how our fat boy and his thin companion were able to adjust their space and time axes with Einstein's β formula so that both found light's velocity to be the same. The c thus kept its constant, invariable property. Now if the relativity of space and time is as valid in the worldly four-dimensional continuum as it was proved to be in empty space on the Cartesian coordinate, the path of a particle (which plays here the role of points on the coordinate) must also have an invariable, objective value; it must also be the same for any two observers who adjust their time and space axes accordingly.

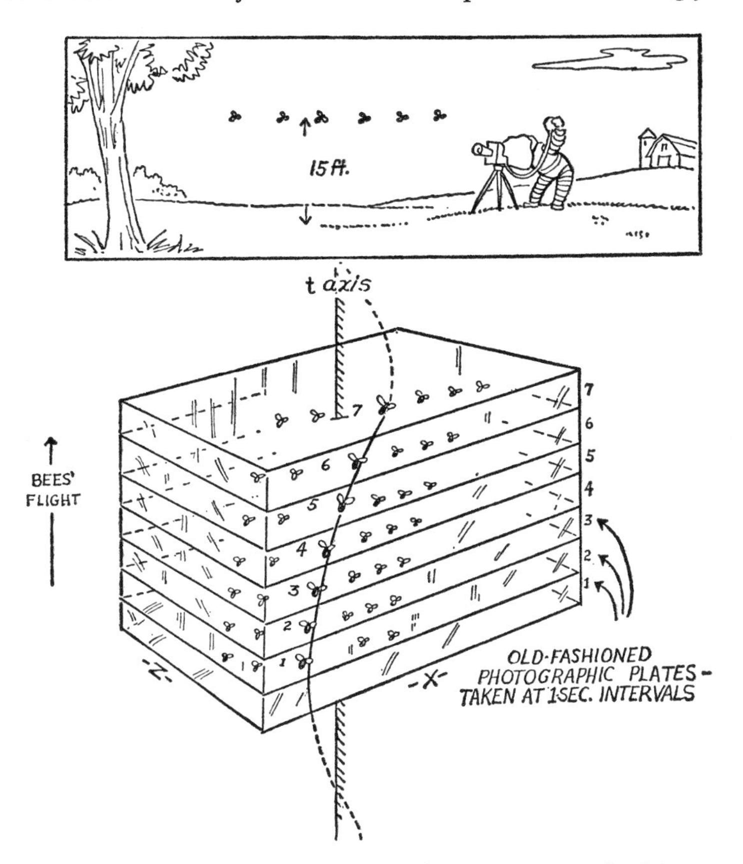

Figure 19. The *world line* of Bee No. 3 during seven seconds of its existence in spacetime.

Let us therefore consider the actual path of a moving particle in a four-dimensional continuum. There, the particle's path may be called its *world line* because it faithfully describes its passage through the world of space and time. For this observation we shall use a kind of pictorial four-dimensional graph.

Although such a graph would be impossible in real life, our unlimited imagination, which is the most useful piece of our equipment, allows us to suppose that we can indeed invent one. Accordingly, let us say that we encounter a swarm of bees in a field and we wish to photograph them at successive intervals during their flight (Fig. 19). Let's also suppose that all of the bees are flying at the same height. Knowing this vertical distance to be 15 feet allows us, for the moment, to eliminate the Y or height axis (which is the real vertical coordinate) and use the vertical axis for time.

We shall take our successive pictures of the bees on old-fashioned photographic plates which, you will remember, have considerable thickness. Now, as the bees fly across the field we shall photograph them once every second until we have seven exposures of the bees' successive positions in level flight. We then place the plates one on top of the other so that their horizontal (frontal) edges form an X axis, and their side edges form a Z axis. The thickness of the plates now becomes the vertical t axis. If we unite the successive positions of one bee (say Bee No. 3 in a line of bees) on the 3 axes we will get a continuous curve representing the path of this bee in space and time. This then is Bee No. 3's world line for seven seconds of its existence in spacetime. It naturally follows that an accumulation of all the world lines of all the bees forms the entire swarm's four-dimensional continuum.

The world line of any bee could have an objective and invariable value if it is the shortest distance between points on the continuum. The shortest distance, you would say, is a straight line. However, we just stated that the path of our bee is a continuous curve. Let us resolve this problem of straightness.

Suppose, with a great deal of patience, we succeeded in training one of our bees so that it always walks in a straight line along a chessboard, the various squares of which allow us to control the

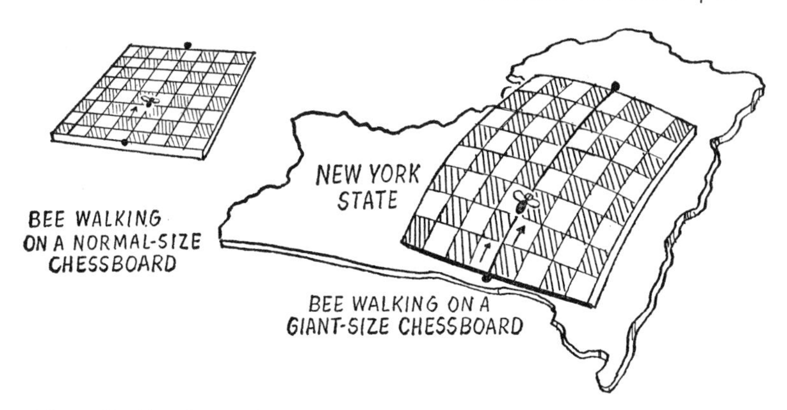

Figure 20. The shortest line connecting two points is not always a straight line.

straightness of the bee's walk (Fig. 20). Now is the bee actually walking in a "straight" line as it passes square after square? We say that apparently it is. Suppose, however, that with the aid of our special equipment we enlarge our chessboard so that it assumes first the proportions and also the form of the island of Manhattan, then the entire state of New York. Eventually we begin to see that the bee, still plodding wearily along as he was trained in a "straight" line, is actually following the curve of the earth's spherical surface. Thus the shortest distance connecting two points on the surface of a sphere is *not* a straight line but a curved one. Any sailor knows that to make the shortest voyage between two points on the ocean he must sail along curved lines called *geodesics*. They are, in fact, "spherical" straight lines.

Can we now, with any real effectiveness, use our "straight-lined" Cartesian coordinate system? Presumably not! In describing the path of continuous motion in a pictorial way—as do differential equations in terms of mathematics—the so-called Gaussian curvilinear coordinates are very appropriate. On a straight-lined coordinate system any definition of distinct positions and time intervals of material points of separate events are possible. On a curvilinear coordinate system, however, continuous events are presented which are almost "there" and almost "then" in juxtaposition with their neighboring events so that together they form a continuum.

Look at Figure 21 and you will see the essential pictorial difference between a purely three-dimensional coordinate system and one of four coordinates. The rigid doll is posed on a straight-lined or Cartesian coordinate with only length, width and height, while the dancing girl is "alive" because she moves through successive time intervals.

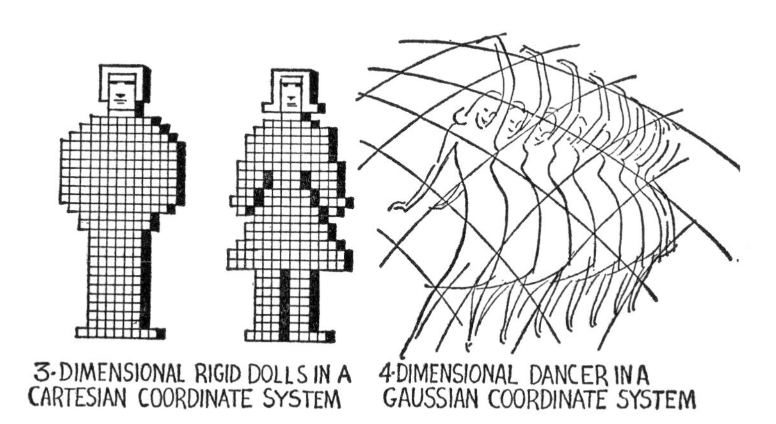

Figure 21. Unlike the rigid dolls, the dancing girl is "alive" because she moves through successive time intervals.

Einstein, when he came to the conclusion that the world lines of particles are geodesics, stated that they are indeed constant and objective to any two observers (as light velocity had been for the fat boy and his thin friend) when the two observers adjust their respective axes (as the boys did).

No one of course is capable of seeing the accumulation of world lines, just as no one can "see" the orbit of the earth moving around the sun, yet the four-dimensional continuum is nevertheless a physical reality where series of continuous four-dimensional events take place.

It is at this point that the relativity theory must stand or fall. Yet, while the relativity principle agrees with experience in the case of constant motion (inasmuch as there is no way for an observer inside such a moving system to perceive this motion), this seems to be untrue in the case of *uneven* motion. Every commuter, for example, notices changes in the direction or speed of his train although he is inside it.

We shall see in the next chapter whether this apparent contradiction cannot be resolved.

CHAPTER △ FOURTEEN

ELEVATORS IN SPACE

INERTIAL LAW & NON-UNIFORM MOTION

ACCELERATION & GRAVITATION

EINSTEIN'S PRINCIPLE OF EQUIVALENCE

A primary characteristic of relativity is that there is no way to determine the motion of a system while inside it. Yet the validity of the relativity principle seems highly questionable in the case of non-uniform or uneven motion because no comparison with other systems is necessary to become aware of changes in uneven motion. Your body, for example, reacts instantly when the engineer of a train applies his brakes or makes a sudden turn; acceleration, deceleration, and change in direction seldom go unnoticed. This tendency to "resist" changes in motion was determined long ago by Newton when he stated that every body continues its motion or remains at rest unless compelled by some force to change its state. Does this "law of inertia" imply that non-uniform motion is an absolute and not a relative concept? Could such a world, pondered Einstein, have been created where exceptional laws of nature exist? A firm believer in a supreme harmony in nature, he answered *no!*

Einstein suspected that although anyone can perceive changes in an accelerated motion, no one can tell whether an observed effect of it is really due to this acceleration or to something else known as *gravitational force.*

This effect was first determined by Newton when he published his Law of Universal Gravitation in 1689, which was a kind of compromise between his law of inertia, which we just mentioned, and Galileo's law of falling bodies. Newton stated that the force necessary to accelerate a body depends upon its mass. Galileo's law was the result of his legendary experiment in Pisa. There he was supposed to have demonstrated that bodies fall at the same rate regardless of their mass. Newton's law said that this was so because the force which he called gravitation pulled bodies toward the ground and increased with the mass of the attracted bodies.

This perfect interplay of gravitation and inertia became the basis of modern mechanics, yet it caused Einstein much puzzlement. He found that the force of gravitation not merely seemed to be but actually was equal to acceleration.

For physicists, not only changes in the amount of speed but also changes in direction are considered to be acceleration. In this sense, centripetal force follows the same requirements for inertia as does gravitation. Acceleration, as a matter of fact, is often mistaken for gravitational attraction by pilots, since it has the same effect on their instruments as gravitation.

Again, if you are suddenly pushed against your seat in a Pullman car you would be sure that this was caused by a sudden acceleration of the train (Fig. 22). Actually, suppose it had been caused by the gravitational pull of a large asteroid which had suddenly come to rest on the tracks behind the train. Being inside the train, you could not tell whether the sudden thrust was due to the asteroid's gravitational pull or the accelerative will of the engineer.

By the same token, if you were a space traveler and felt the same sudden backward thrust, you would be hard put (unless you were the pilot) to say whether it was due to the ship's acceleration or the gravitational tug of a passing giant comet.

Uneven motion, then, is no more of an absolute than the ideal of constant velocity without acceleration. Why? Because the effects of various non-uniform motions cannot be distinguished from the effects of gravitation and thus cannot be determined by themselves in an absolute way. In this case, relativistic dynamics may also be valid for non-uniform motion.

The fact that gravitation and acceleration seem equivalent means (in principle), as Einstein stated in his *principle of equivalence,* that the field of force which would be created by gravitation is in every way equivalent to a field created by accelerated motion; there would be no way whatsoever to distinguish between them.

To understand this fully, let's suppose that two men—one an experienced spaceman and the other a youthful space cadet—arrive at a place in outer space where there is no gravitation (Fig. 23).

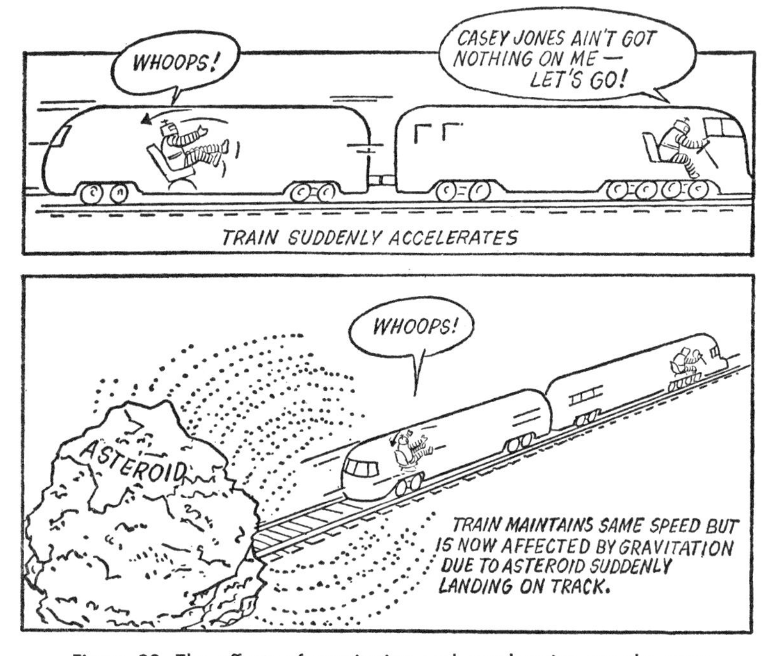

Figure 22. The effects of gravitation and acceleration are the same.

If one man pushes the other, the one pushed sails merrily through space; if one lets go of a monkey wrench, it does not fall, but simply floats. Everything behaves according to the law of inertia. Each body retains its state of uniform motion or of rest unless acted upon. In this inertial utopia, our space travelers chance to come upon an elevator freely floating in space and immediately recognize it as the one with which Einstein himself proved his law of equivalence.

The elevator being a bit outmoded since Einstein's day, our two spacemen decide to modernize it by providing it with single-vision glass walls. Thus someone inside the elevator cannot see outside, but an observer outside can see everything happening within the elevator. Deciding to test Einstein's theory for themselves, the younger of the two enters the reconditioned elevator while the elder spaceman remains on a space platform outside. In free space, of course, the cadet is weightless (Fig. 23A).

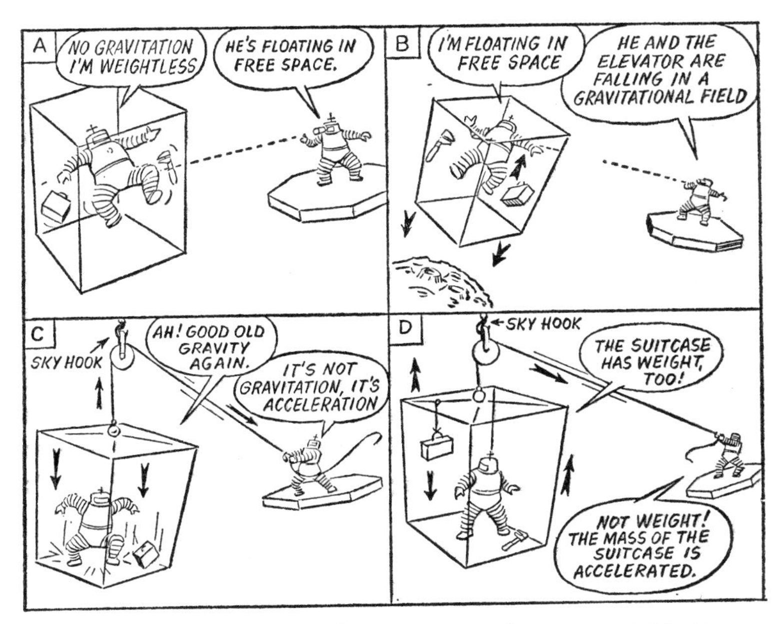

Figure 23. Gravitation and acceleration are merely two ways of looking at the same thing.

Now the elder spaceman, unknown to the cadet, moves the elevator into a varying gravitational field (Fig. 23B). The elevator, of course, begins to fall freely downward according to gravitational law. Since the walls of the elevator are of single-vision glass, the young space cadet cannot see what is happening outside. The elder spaceman, however, looking into the elevator, sees that the younger one does not notice a thing at first; the cadet continues to float weightlessly, together with all other objects inside the elevator. Thus, for someone inside a non-uniformly moving system there is apparently no way to distinguish between falling in a gravitational field or floating in empty space. Eventually, however, were the elevator to accelerate faster and faster toward the gravitational body, the cadet would find himself flying toward the ceiling.

Next the experienced spaceman fixes a cable to the elevator and causes it to rise in accelerated motion (Fig. 23C). Abruptly, the young cadet lands on the floor and so do all the objects which were weightless before.

The experienced spaceman, watching him from outside, knows that the elevator is accelerating upward by a motive force, but the cadet inside the elevator simply says:

"Everything has weight again. I am now obviously inside a gravitational field."

Evidently then Einstein is correct in saying that, given such conditions, the *effects* of gravitation and acceleration are the same and cannot be distinguished from each other.

Another of Einstein's conclusions was that weight, too, must be principally and not accidentally equivalent to mass. This becomes clear when the cadet—still accelerating upward—ties his suitcase to a rope attached to the ceiling of the elevator (Fig. 23D). The rope immediately becomes taut.

"This is because of the weight of the suitcase," asserts the cadet. "It is inside a gravitational field the same as I am."

The experienced spaceman however, still observing the elevator from outside, declares:

"The rope is taut because the mass of the suitcase is also participating in the accelerated, upward motion of the elevator."

Many statements of general relativity were later proved by empirical facts, but the principle of equivalence of masses and weights was demonstrated experimentally in 1909, years *before* the appearance of the Theory of General Relativity, in a brilliant paper by Lorant Eotvos. This Hungarian physicist showed, with the aid of a sensitive "torsion" pendulum, that gravitational effects exerted upon two spheres of identical weights but of different masses do not differ from each other.

Our next chapter will furnish us with additional proofs of Einstein's Theory of General Relativity.

CHAPTER △ FIFTEEN

PROOFS OF GENERAL RELATIVITY

MERCURY'S STRANGE ORBIT

THE CURVATURE OF LIGHT RAYS

We have seen that Einstein, in expanding his Theory of Special Relativity, discovered that the effect of great masses of matter on bodies near them—known as gravitational force—is the same as the effect of accelerated motion. With this statement he encompassed a whole range of mechanical theories in one single systematic law.

His next step was to show how his new theory of gravitation differed from Newton's classical law of universal gravitation. Newton, after years of observation, found that gravitational force is directly proportional to the mass of bodies involved and inversely proportional to the square of the distance between them. His constant quantity g, the gravitational constant, also became the basis for determining "gravity," or the force of gravitational attraction between celestial bodies. This force is what keeps the planets in their orbits without allowing them to fly off into space.

The orbits of planets were thought to be circular by Copernicus but were later proved to be elliptical by Kepler. Neither he nor Newton, however, could say why this was so. Experimentation seemed to justify Newton's statement that these elliptical orbits were fixed, and that the planets cover the same paths again and again as they go through space.

Einstein's numerical findings, however, differed slightly from Newton's. He proposed that, instead of believing that masses of bodies exert forces upon each other at a distance, it was more realistic to assume that this is in reality the result of the variations which space itself suffers about great masses. Einstein also stated that the elliptical orbits of planets are not actually fixed at all, as Newton's mechanics suggested, but are slowly rotating around their longer axes in the opposite direction to the revolving motion of the planets.

This rotation is difficult to observe in most astronomical cases. Our earth, for instance, is too distant from the sun, its rotation too slow, its orbit almost circular. Only planets with very flat and very "elliptical" orbits, rotating at high orbital velocities near the sun, present observable excess rotation. The best example is the planet Mercury, which is closest of all to the sun (Fig. 24). Einstein calculated that, during a 100-year period of rotation, the major axis of Mercury's orbit must turn almost 43 angular seconds. His calculation was later proved to be in accord with observation.

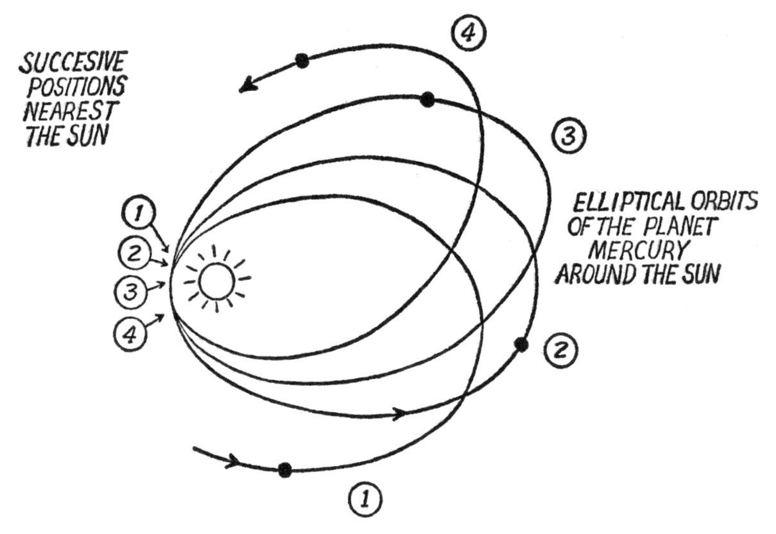

Figure 24. The strange orbital motion of the planet Mercury is a proof of General Relativity.

For a long time astronomers had pondered about Mercury's peculiar rotation. Leverrier, a French scientist, suggested more than a century ago that this odd orbital motion could be caused by the effect of other, as yet undiscovered, planets. Subsequently, Neptune and Pluto were discovered as a result of this effect; yet no such planetary action could be discovered in the vicinity of Mercury. Its odd rotation could be explained only by Einstein's equations.

The solving of this cosmic puzzle became one of the proofs of General Relativity. Yet the real impact of General Relativity lies not in having provided accepted explanations for many long-noticed but enigmatic natural phenomena but in identifying gravitational and dynamic effects, thus plausibly explaining the true path of moving matter. If such paths can be calculated with great accuracy, the world lines of all material bodies, including the orbital motion of the planets, can also be determined.

Planets, Einstein stated, do not follow elliptical orbits because of the effects of gravity, but because these are the shortest paths for them. "Shortest paths" and "gravity" are two ways of looking at the same thing. In fact, all bodies have an inherent natural tendency to follow the shortest possible paths while in motion.

Now the shortest distance between two paths in three-dimensional space seems to follow a straight line, as we demonstrated earlier in the case of our chessboard. However, when its magnitude became substantially comparable to the earth, the straight line became a *geodesic* or curved line, its curvature following that of the earth's spheroidal surface. Now Einstein stated the path of motion is curved when it enters the vicinity of great masses, for the space around them is also curved.

Space, we learned, is not three- but four-dimensional. The curved path which anything in motion must thus follow in space is the shortest four-dimensional distance. It is *not* identical with the shortest three-dimensional distance. We saw how different three- and four-dimensional distances were when studying their respective systems.

When, in electromagnetic fields, material properties like mass were not considered, the direction of all radiation, light included, could be determined as a straight one. The field, however, in which gravitational events take place—the *gravitational field*—does not exist in a vacuum but around material bodies. Similarly, space and time considered in matterless emptiness by the Special Theory of

Relativity was based upon the constant velocity of light; and light's direction there was taken to be straight. Yet the spacetime continuum, considered by the General Theory of Relativity, is in the vicinity of great masses, not in a hypothetical vacuum. Thus, whether considered from the gravitational field's viewpoint or from the four-dimensional continuum's viewpoint, the result remains the same: the path of anything moving in space, light included, may be curvilinear, whether compelled by gravitation or by the curvature of space through which it moves.

Special Relativity proved that energy possesses mass. Light being energy (hence, having mass, too), it is easy to understand that the direction of its motion is influenced by the gravitational field or, if you prefer, by the properties of the varying four-dimensional spacetime continuum.

That light has weight was empirically proved by so-called *radiation pressure*—the slight, yet real pressure light exerts when falling on a surface. Obviously, then, the curvature of light rays passing near great masses also needed empirical proof. Now the masses of earthly bodies were not great enough to cause noticeable deflections; however, said Einstein, starlight passing near the sun ought to exhibit a slightly deflected path. The very faint light of such a star, however, is only observable near the sun at the time of a solar eclipse.

When a total solar eclipse came in 1919, World War I prevented Einstein from participating in one of the two expeditions sent to Africa and Brazil to confirm this theory. It fell to two Englishmen, Cromellin and Eddington, to confirm Einstein's calculations. They obtained this proof by photographing the light from two stars with special cameras. The first pictures were taken when the stars were not near the sun and showed no deflection in the paths of their lights; technically speaking, the angular distance measurement was zero degrees.

On two subsequent pictures, taken when the stars were in the vicinity of the sun, the stars appeared to be shifted away from the sun because their light was bent *toward* it, causing the angular measurement to become *more* than zero.

Now, was there any way of deciding whether the above-described proofs of General Relativity were due to the effects of gravitation or to curvature which the spacetime continuum suffers near the huge celestial bodies? Knowing that the effects of these two phenomena are the same, the answer had to be *no*.

Using our Guided Tour equipment again, let us perform an experiment to show how a varying curvature of the spacetime continuum can be mistaken for the presence of an actual physical force like gravitation. Let us say that I am standing on a clay tennis court and you are hovering three or four hundred feet above it (Fig. 25). (During this experiment you will *not* be permitted to use your telescope—*only* your naked eye!) On the tennis court below I have two tennis balls. I roll one of them toward a slight bump in the court so that it strikes the right part of the bump. Then, of course, the ball deflects to the right. The second ball I roll toward a slight

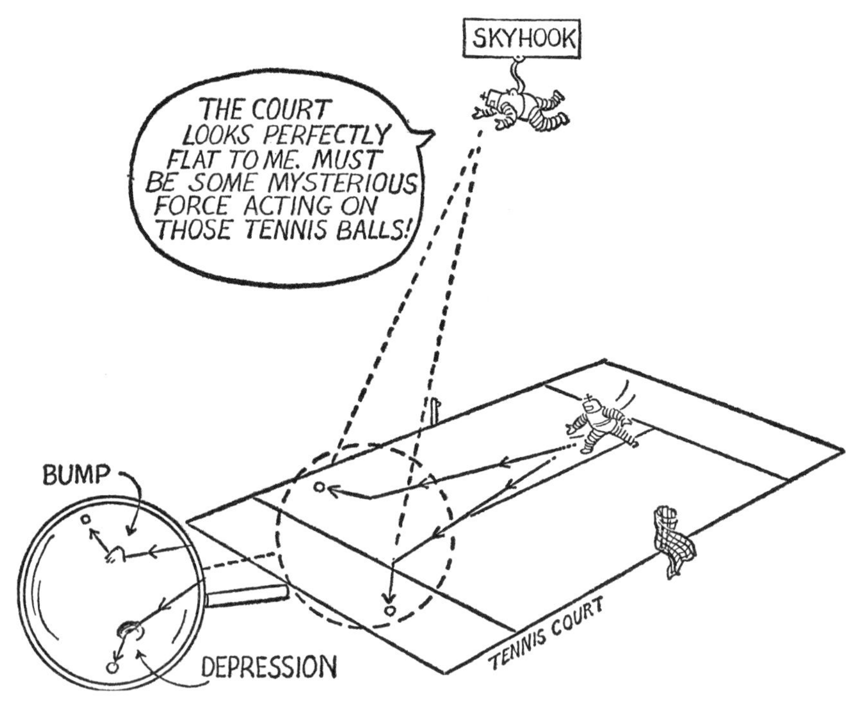

Figure 25. Here it is distance which causes the mistaken impression of an actual physical force at work. Insert shows simple explanation of tennis balls' behavior.

depression in the court so that it goes into the right side of the depression. It, of course, caroms off to the left. Far above the court, however, you are not able to tell a slight bump from a slight depression; in fact, the court appears perfectly flat. When the two tennis balls fly off in different directions, you may tend to think this is due to some mysterious attractive or repulsive physical force.

In exactly the same manner, Einstein pointed out, the force we normally interpret as gravitation may actually be the effect produced by the curvature of the four-dimensional space-time continuum operating near large celestial bodies like the sun.

We shall see more of how such four-dimensional geometry operates in succeeding chapters. First, however, we shall decide whether all principles of relativity hold in our world when considered as a four-dimensional continuum, and also whether the General Theory of Relativity solved all the problems of the universe.

CHAPTER △ SIXTEEN

THE RELATIVISTIC MERRY-GO-ROUND

THE EFFECT OF MASS

CLOCKS ON THE SUN

EUCLID'S 5TH POSTULATE

In the four-dimensional continuum of our world, the role played by the constant velocity of light in empty space was replaced by the path of motion. This quantity had to be like light's velocity in the Special Theory of Relativity, that is, the same for any observers in the world, provided they adjust their space and time axes accordingly.

It is clear that this adjustment cannot be as simple as in the case of straight-lined uniform motion. That is, Einstein's quantity β would not suffice here. Identification of gravitational and dynamic effects proved that no such thing as absolute motion exists. Thus the entire principle of relativity also holds in the case of non-uniform accelerated motion in a space where varying influences of different masses exist. Therefore, in this four-dimensional spacetime continuum curving about great masses, space and time axes depend not only on velocity but also on the effect of these same masses.

In the vicinity of such masses, this effect can be so significant that the interval between two events may change radically when measured on different spacetime graphs. For example, an earthly historian would say that the Declaration of Independence was signed in America thirteen years before the seizure of the Bastille in Europe (Fig. 26). Yet an alien astronomer observing our earth from a distant solar system, might render an entirely different opinion. He might find, depending on how the path of his planet is influenced by masses of the universe, that the two events were simultaneous. The two events, in fact, might even appear to him as happening in the very same place. Also, if he does not adjust his spacetime axes properly, he might mistake terrestrial spacetime intervals for mere spatial distances or time intervals.

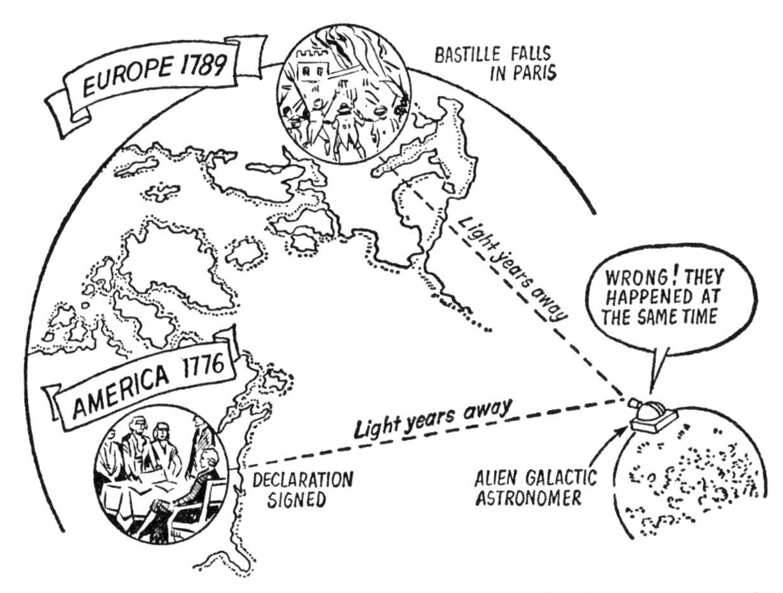

Figure 26. Two terrestrial events, viewed by an alien galactic astronomer, might appear to him as happening simultaneously.

For instance, our alien astronomer might view the signing of the Declaration of Independence not as an event in time at all, but simply as a material body—say a box so long, so high, and so wide. On the other hand, he might view it as simply a time interval in which a shadowy John Hancock is perpetually applying his signature to a document that seems not to be there at all.

This is not so astonishing if we remember that space concepts concerning celestial occurrences, like the orbits of planets, changed as a result of measurements suggested in the Theory of General Relativity. We shall now add another proof to show how time concepts are also altered under the effect of great masses.

It is a proven fact that all time processes are considerably slowed down in the neighborhood of great material masses. Einstein calculated that a clock located on the sun would run one second slower in a six-day period, compared with a similar clock on earth. We cannot of course take real clocks to the sun; we can, however, prove that mass has an influence on time. Professor Irving Ives, an American scientist, had previously demonstrated how time indeed slowed down as predicted by the Special Theory of Relativity. Ives accelerated hydrogen atoms in an electrical field inside a tube until they moved with about one six-thousandth of the velocity of light. Even this "moderate" speed was enough for Ives to observe that each vibration of an electron of the hydrogen atom was *longer* when the hydrogen atom was moving. Just as differently vibrating strings produce different tones, so different atoms each have their individual vibrations. And just as a slower string vibration produces a lower tone, so did the frequency of atomic vibration decrease when the hydrogen atom moved with the above-mentioned velocity—proving that time actually slowed down as a result of this velocity. In a similar manner, the vibration time of radiations on the sun would be slower due to the sun's greater mass, compared with the vibration time of the same kind of radiation on earth. Einstein thus predicted the shifting of sunlight toward the red end of the spectrum compared with light coming from an earthly source—a result of the slowing down of time on the sun.

To prove this, however, sunlight had to be substituted by the light of a more "massive" star, the sun's mass not being "massive" enough and hence its shift too small. Sirius B is a small star; however, its density is 25,000 times greater than that of the sun. Using its faint light, W. S. Adams, another American, proved that time on Sirius B flows much slower than it does on earth. Now this "relativistic shift" caused by mass is more considerable than that caused simply by high velocity. Thus, Lt. Farnsworth, our bridegroom of Chapter One, could indeed stay young enough to marry his underage fiancée were he to spend a certain amount of time on Sirius B. The lieutenant, however, would grow in mass and gain so much in weight that it is doubtful he would be an acceptable candidate for his bride's hand after all.

Let us again use our equipment to investigate the matter of how space and time are altered under the influence of masses. Since General Relativity allows us to choose among systems, regardless of how uneven their motion, let us now deal with a very irregular one. Such a system might be a combination merry-go-round and "Snap-the-Whip" whose coaches not only extend outward from a center but also rotate merry-go-round fashion (Fig. 27). Such a rotating device,

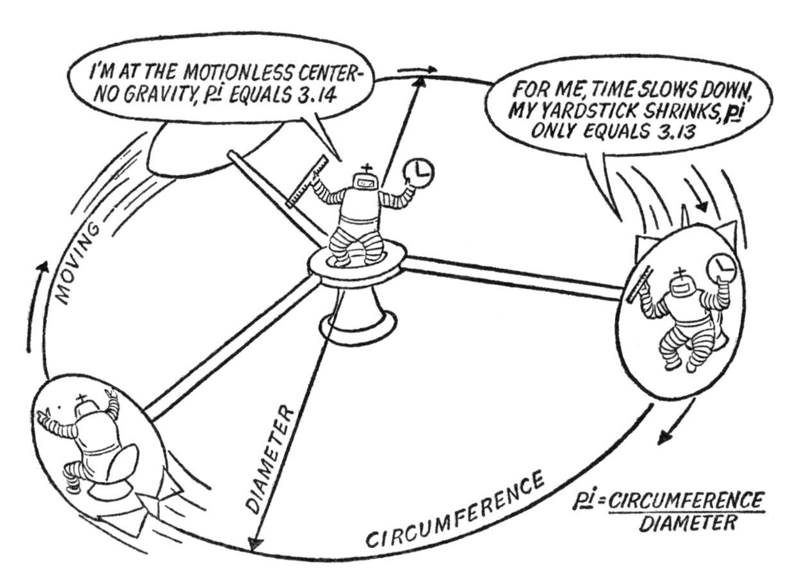

Figure 27. An experiment with a "Snap-the-Whip" merry-go-round, showing how geometry is altered by mass and motion.

from the outside, would clearly appear to an observer as an unevenly accelerating system. From inside the coaches, however, assuming they had no windows, a rider would feel that he was in some sort of gravitational system which is strongest at the outside orbital circumference. The very center of this device, however, would be motionless and hence would exert no gravitational effect.

The set of coaches now rotates with high velocity in a circular orbit. We shall also postulate that this motion is uniform, which of course it would not be in a real-life experiment. On the circumference now, any yardstick the rider may have with him would shrink, and his watch would slow down. To the rider, the cause of this may be due to gravitation; to an outside observer, it may be due to centripetal force. It does not matter which is right, for the effects are the same.

Similar yardsticks and watches located at any point along the arm supporting any coach (the radius of the circle) would experience different alterations in shrinkage and time. This is so because the radius is midway between the strong motion or field of gravitation at the circumference, and the motionless center where there is no gravitation.

Now we know that if we divide the circumference of a circle by its diameter we get a constant ratio known as *pi,* roughly equal to 3.14. When our entire merry-go-round is at rest and we perform this calculation upon the geometrical system it describes, we indeed get *pi,* or 3.14. But once the merry-go-round moves, the gravitational or centrifugal forces being (1) strong around the circumference, (2) non-existent in the center and (3) uneven at various points along the diameter, the above-mentioned division will *not* yield *pi* at all, but a lesser quantity!

This means that the geometry of spacetime, when altered by masses, is not the geometry to which we are normally accustomed. That is, it is not the classical Euclidian plane geometry but is, in fact, a new geometry which considers points, lines, planes and bodies not as one-, two- or three-dimensional abstract figures but as events, paths and orbits of continuous motion which is distorted by neighboring masses. This is what is known as *four-dimensional geometry.*

The *resemblance* between a mathematical circle, for instance, and an apparently "circular" object for centuries substantiated Euclid's "postulates." They were accepted as self-evident truths. No one contested, for example, that a straight line could be drawn from one point to any other one or that all right angles were equal to one another. One of Euclid's Postulates, however, the Fifth, could never be derived from the others. This stated that "through a given point only one straight line can be drawn parallel to another given line, not passing through that point." For centuries mathematicians tried to prove this but never succeeded.

Finally, in the middle of the last century, Janos Bolyai, a young Hungarian officer, stated in a short paper that the Fifth Postulate cannot be proved because it is *not true*—at least not exclusively. Bolyai's results and also those of a Russian mathematician, Lobatchewsky, proved that in addition to "Euclidian" geometry, many other geometries are possible where the sum of the angles of a triangle is not 180° but *less*.

The idea that non-Euclidian geometries could be created without abolishing the whole geometrical edifice slumbered until Bernhard Riemann, a German mathematician, constructed two new geometries. With them, he was able to show that the sum of the angles of the triangle is *more* than 180°, and also that there are no possible parallel lines.

We have already distinguished between two-dimensional and three-dimensional geometries when we dealt with two- and three-dimensional "plane" and "space" coordinates. If we search for the main difference on the two-dimensional level between Euclidian and non-Euclidian geometries, we immediately notice that Euclid drew his geometrical figures on plane surfaces such as a sheet of paper, while Riemann drew his on the surface of a sphere, such as a globe of the world. Also, Riemann was able to do this on a higher dimensional level. It was Riemann's geometry, in fact, which permitted Einstein to define his four-dimensional continuum.

We shall attempt to explain its basic theory in our next chapter.

CHAPTER △ SEVENTEEN

BACKGAMMON BOARDS, PAPER DOLLS AND DANCING GIRLS

NEGATIVE & POSITIVE CURVATURE

NON-EUCLIDIAN GEOMETRIES

TWO-, THREE-, & FOUR-DIMENSIONAL WORLDS

SUPER-DIMENSIONS

When we are dealing with simple Euclidian planes, such as those on our small chessboard of an earlier chapter, parallel lines seem to be entirely possible. Also, if we draw any triangle on the small chessboard, the sum of its angles will always be 180°.

Let us suppose, however, that instead of the chessboard we now have a *very* large, thick, transparent Plexiglas backgammon board. For the sake of convenience, we shall assume that both sides of the board have been imprinted with the traditional triangles used in playing backgammon. Now if we heat the backgammon board until it is in a plastic state and press it against some curved surface it will assume a bowl-like shape (Fig. 28). The concave inside of the "bowl" thus formed is called *negative curvature;* the convex outside surface is known as *positive curvature.* Naturally all of the triangles on the latter board are now curved, too, and the lines forming them have become geodesic lines.

Examining these lines on the curved backgammon board, we notice that certain things are no longer geometrically true compared to when the board was a simple plane. For example, the sides of neighboring triangles which were formerly parallel to each other are no longer so. Again, if we attempt to connect two "parallel" lines with a perpendicular, the resulting angles do not form 90° angles; actually, they are *more* or *less* than 90° depending on whether they are on the positive or negative side of the board.

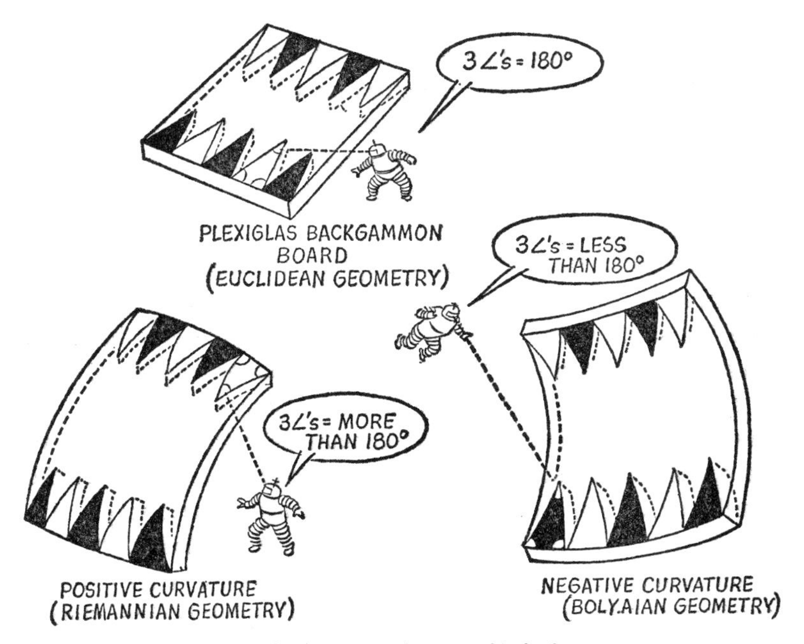

Figure 28. There is more than one kind of geometry.

Looking at the "triangles" on the negatively-curved side of the board and measuring their angles with a protractor, we find that their sum is *less* than 180°. Also, we find that it *is* possible to draw parallel lines, but they are only parallel for a little while; if extended they would eventually meet. The circumference of any circle described on the curved surface would not be proportional to the diameter, and, as in the case of our merry-go-round, the concept of the Euclidian ratio *pi* no longer holds. Also, the area of the circle is not proportional to the square of the diameter, but increases faster. Such negative curvature is the basis of Bolyai's geometry.

If we turn our attention now to the positive side of the Plexiglas backgammon board we discover yet another geometry prevails. Assuming that the outer or positive curvature of the board has taken a spherical shape, all of the lines of the triangles now represent the arcs of great circles. Since any two of them will ultimately intersect, no parallel lines can exist. Also, the sum of the angles of any of the backgammon triangles will not be equal to 180°, as in Euclidian plane geometry, but will be *more* than this figure. In addition, the circumference of any circle described on the board is not proportional to its diameter; that is, the area of the circle increases more slowly than the square of the diameter. This is the geometry of Riemann and many of its postulates may be checked on any child's globe of the world.

Now, curved three-dimensional space is merely a geometrical generalization of a curvilinear two-dimensional plane such as a spherical surface. Yet while we are able to judge what is below us (in number of dimensions) we are often unable to comprehend what is above us. We, who are three-dimensional human beings, can look down quite comfortably on a two-dimensional presentation, yet we are apt to become quite uncomfortable when asked to visualize the fourth geometrical dimension—which of course is necessary to examine space correctly. It seems that Gauss, often called the "prince of mathematicians," was right when he said that it is an inherent peculiarity of the human mind that it can only think in three dimensions.

In addition, the non-Euclidian geometry Einstein used to describe physical phenomena of the spacetime continuum is not "simple," non-varying, homogeneous space but a varying one which depends on how far away or how close it is to great masses. Also, no device of our amazing equipment can help us visualize the differences between varying dimensions except our imaginative sense of the abstract. Why? Because we are actually not dealing with physical phenomena but with mathematical objects.

Let us go, therefore, into a make-believe theater where three unusual movies are being shown. First we shall see a cartoon depicting a world of two-dimensional beings. Next, a historical documentary about a purely three-dimensional world. Finally we shall see a science-fiction film called "The Fascination of the Fourth Dimension."

As the lights dim and the first film begins, we see a group of curious two-dimensional cartoon beings projected on nothing more than a sheet of paper (Fig. 29). These people are completely flat

Figure 29. People in a two-dimensional world would resemble paper dolls.

and, having no thickness at all, are consequently unable even to imagine that dimension. They can only move back and forth, right and left, on the level of their plane. However, they are quite intelligent! Some of them are performing measurements with one-dimensional "yardsticks," all of which, however, are plain straight lines. As depth does not exist for them, they cannot turn themselves about. To perform pirouettes, for instance, they would need a third dimension; otherwise, they must remain in their two-dimensional world.

These people may appear odd to the adults in the theater, yet they seem perfectly natural to the children present, for children are used to playing with paper dolls whose backs are not colored by crayons. Children are quite content to play in a two-dimensional world, and, indeed, to turn their paper dolls around to color their "backs" never occurs to them.

The difference between us, the audience, who are three-dimensional, and the two-dimensional beings of the cartoon is even greater than that which separated Gulliver from the Lilliputians. For if the Lilliputians viewed Gulliver as a giant, they nevertheless *saw* him; our two-dimensional beings, however, are incapable of perceiving us in our bodily appearance. They possess just one dimension too few to be able to do this.

If, however, the cartoon were being filmed "live" on TV and someone in the theater lit a cigarette, the two-dimensional people would see only its glowing end. To them it would look like a new two-dimensional sun entering their world. Also, were we to approach their paper world too closely it is entirely possible that our own gravitational mass would cause it to fly towards us.

As the cartoon progresses, we see that the two-dimensional people have no sense of time either and are, in fact, unaware of their own eternal, lifeless existence. They are simply satisfied to make trips to the edges of their sheet of paper; beyond this nothing exists for them. They are thus convinced that their plane world is finite; it does not occur to them that, together with their two-dimensional system, they are actually imbedded in three-dimensional space.

Now someone in the cartoon—a three-dimensional being—takes pity on the monotony of their existence and glues together the two edges of their sheet of paper, making a cylinder out of it without top or bottom. Now the two-dimensional people are no longer forced to return from their trips to the edge of the paper but can make complete round trips. If there were a scientist among them he could now state that their finite world had suddenly become infinite. It is now a curvilinear surface of nothingness where straight lines, when surface and lines are sufficiently magnified, become curved. Yet, as the cartoon people are still unable to conceive of depth, their geometrical concept does not basically change. At this point, the cartoon ends.

The second film is the historical documentary of the three-dimensional world and the audience must look through the eyes of a four-dimensional observer. To get a true picture of any dimensional system, we must examine it *from at least one dimension higher.*

Accordingly, an usher passes down the aisle and distributes a pair of four-dimensional spectacles to each movie-goer. We put them on and as the film commences see that we are watching the pageant of mankind's history. Since we are watching it from a higher dimension, however, it looks rather queer.

Men of Antiquity appear to be slowly moving dolls on extremely tiny parts of our terrestrial sphere. They look exactly like the little figures of different nationalities so often seen on miniature globes in travel bureau windows. (They also greatly resemble the rigid three-dimensional doll of an earlier chapter.)

Among them we see geometricians, like Euclid, making accurate measurements in small areas not great enough to follow the earth's curvature. Now, considering such doll-like people as placed on planes, their geometrical concept resembles that of the two-dimensional people before their world was "glued" together. That is, before the discovery of Copernicus, they too considered their world to be finite.

Gradually, however, as the human pageant progresses, sailors set out on voyages to the edges of their plane-like world; slowly it becomes round and the sailors "glue" it together. They now consider their world infinite; however, its Euclidian geometrical abstraction persists for a long time as bodies retain rigid, statuelike shapes, and stars in fixed orbits are scattered throughout the emptiness of space. However, when scientists of our century finally prove that all three-dimensional existence is but a motion in the fourth one—*time*—the rigid bodies become actual events; the zombie-like dolls on the globe begin to move with purpose, just as our lifeless doll became a dancing girl. In a sense, these people take on "life," much as motion picture film did when it replaced individual "still" photos (Fig. 30).

As the picture ends, its message is clear: only by the addition of the fourth dimension of *time* can a three-dimensional world possess "life," for time is, in a way, the motion which cements together the individual events of our existence.

Before the third and final film starts, an usher hands us a pamphlet to read. It explains some things we will need to know before the four-dimensional movie is run. The pamphlet says that a "dimensionless being" or, in reality, a mathematical point would never be capable of entering a one-dimensional or linear world. Likewise, pure length alone could never enter a two-dimensional plane. Again, something which is only two-dimensional could never make the transition to the three-dimensional world. In general, then, a lower dimensional "thing" can never enter into a world of a higher dimension; however, a higher dimensional "thing" is always capable of entering into a lower dimensional world.

Figure 30. How events are related by time.

To illustrate this, the pamphlet suggests we try an experiment. We draw a circle on a piece of blotting paper with a grease pencil and then wet the portion outside with water. Let us say that the blotter is infinitely thin so as to make the system as nearly two-dimensional as possible. Since the grease pencil is water-repellent, no water can enter the "magic circle." But we, from above in our superior three-dimensional world, can easily wet the inside of the circle by sprinkling water into it. Yet, the water on the blotter below, participating only in a two-dimensional system, could never give itself the third-dimensional depth it needs to enter the circle. The pamphlet also cautions us that there are no physical appearances in the fourth dimension as we know them in the third dimension; it is a realm, too, where no "left" and no "right" exists, nor any "up" or "down" as we know it. Thus, for example, a four-dimensional glove would theoretically fit either hand.

It will help us here, the pamphlet goes on, to perform another experiment. Take a strip of paper about a foot long and one inch wide, give one end of it a full twist and then join the two ends of the strip. We have now what is referred to as a *curve of Moebius,* after the German mathematician. If you trace with your finger from the joining point all the way around the surface of the strip you will experience the sensation of ending up on the opposite side of the paper from which you started. There is a feeling of "reversibility" in this experiment—especially if we color one side of the Moebius strip—which prepares us for a tour of the fourth dimension.

The movie is now about to begin and once again the usher passes out a pair of spectacles to everyone. These, of course, are fifth-dimensional since we need at least one higher dimension if we are to observe the fourth. The film commences rolling.

What would we see, however, *without* the special glasses? Nothing, except nebulous lines of ever-succeeding points. These represent the meeting places, on the vertical axis, of the vertices of three-dimensional spaces which surround four-dimensional appearances. If you recall the illustration of Bee No. 3 of an earlier chapter, you will realize that these succeeding vertices are similar to the *world lines* of the places where physical surfaces would logically meet in the fourth dimension.

The graph of our bee was simplified, however. We omitted the real, spatial vertical axis which marks the third dimension—height. Actually, the surfaces do not meet to surround the fourth dimension; rather, the entire three-dimensional spaces are united on the vertical axis.

The producers of the film, however, sensing our disappointment at seeing nothing but world lines, have arranged for the actors to be injected with a certain fluid which will make their shapes visible to us.

Accordingly, the next scene takes us into a four-dimensional supermarket where we shall assume that a four-dimensional housewife is doing her shopping. Because of the fluid, we see the housewife all right, but all we see of the shelves, products and counters are points at which surfaces meet. In fact, the housewife's shopping cart is jumbled with the points of the purchases she has made. The housewife, however, is having her troubles at the meat counter. The butcher, whom she meets on the time coordinate, is trying to cut her a slice of steak, which is impossible in the fourth dimension. All the butcher is able to do is to cut off minute "world line bits" of the meat at the points where meat bodies intersect on the vertical fourth coordinate. Hence, the most practical form of meat which the four-dimensional housewife would ever be able to serve is a very fine version of hamburger!

Now let us put on the five-dimensional glasses in order to see everything that is going on in the four-dimensional world.

The film shows us other examples of life in the fourth dimension. One scene pictures an operating room where a four-dimensional surgeon is operating on a three-dimensional patient. We are surprised, however, to see that the surgeon has not bothered to open his patient's body. This is because, to him, in a higher dimension, it is *already open*—as our greased blotting paper was "open" to us. In Figure 31, we see how a four-dimensional executive might look seated at his desk, as viewed from the third and fifth dimensions.

In yet another scene a small boy, as yet too young to realize the opportunities of the dimension in which he lives, tries to conceal a poor report card from his parents. His mother and father, however, are only too well aware that he has received an unsatisfactory grade in arithmetic, for, although the card is concealed in the boy's pocket, they can still read it.

The film then ends on a happy note; namely, that there could be no war in the fourth dimension because of the simple fact that any possible menace from three-dimensional enemies or weapons would be immediately known to inhabitants there.

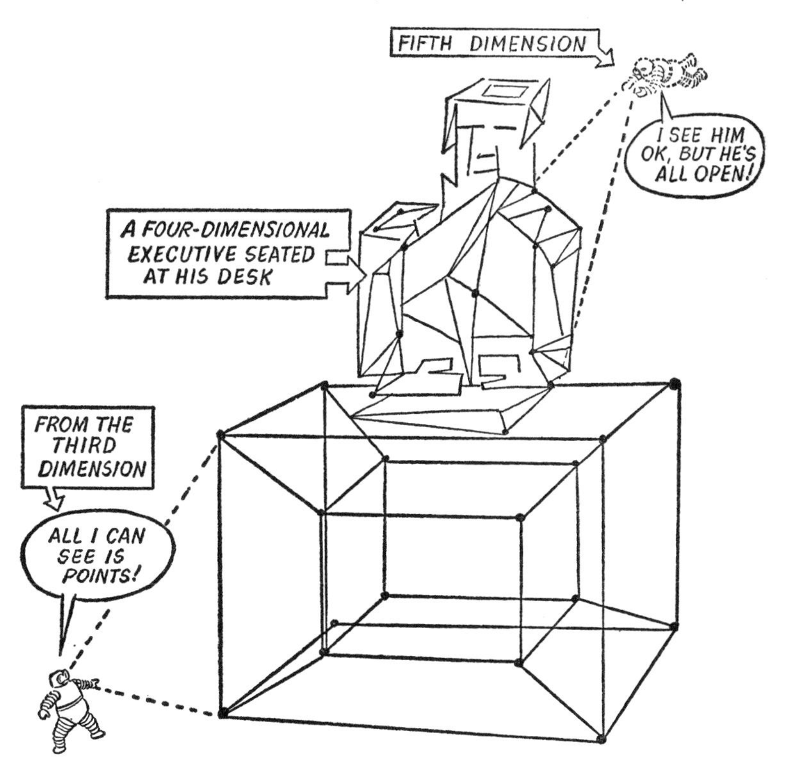

Figure 21. How the fourth dimension might appear from the third and fifth dimensions.

The lesson which we learn from the film is that life as we physically know it could never exist in a purely geometrical fourth dimension. It is only a mathematical possibility.

On the other hand, there is no proof either that such a super-dimension could not exist. Just as our three-dimensional space exists in time, so could a fourth be imbedded in a fifth, a fifth imbedded in a sixth and so on.

Indeed, if super-dimensions did exist, our own sun could be a mere three-dimensional projection of a four-dimensional event, just as our glowing cigarette end seemed to be a circular "sun" in the paper world of our two-dimensional beings.

Does this sound fantastic? Perhaps it only seems so, for our senses have not yet developed highly enough to comprehend higher dimensions than our own.

The frightening aspects of higher dimensional levels can, however, be obviated if we simply suppose that our four-dimensional universe, though seemingly limitless, is not infinite, but finite. This is what Einstein himself suggested. Was he entirely right this time?

To find out, we shall get acquainted with Einstein's universe, and all the theories of the universe which followed.

CHAPTER △ EIGHTEEN

MODELS OF THE UNIVERSE

COSMOGONY

THE EXPANDING UNIVERSE

FINITENESS & INFINITENESS

THE UNIVERSE'S FINAL "DAY"

Worlds of one, two, three or more dimensions, discussed in the last chapter, are mathematically and logically possible. However, pure mathematical concepts can only receive their passports into the realm of natural sciences when their actual physical counterparts are defined. The constant interplay between theory and observation marks the development of *cosmogony,* or the science dealing with the origin of the universe.

Our earth is but one of the planets in our solar system. In turn, the solar system is but one of a vast number of similar ones which, together with other stellar systems, form the *galaxy*. This mind-staggering multitude of stars was, for a long time, believed to be a unique island universe in the immense ocean of empty space. Observation by telescopes and other instruments, together with calculations, proved, however, that far away from our own stellar island in distant space similar galaxies and giant nebulae also exist. The more distant they are, the fainter they appear to us; thus, the degree of their brightness became one of the measuring rods of their remoteness. The distribution of individual galaxies seemed to be irregular, but when larger volumes of space were observed their arrangement was found to follow a distinct pattern. This led to the belief that the composition of the universe as a whole is uniform and that by studying sample parts of our own world, we would learn universal truths.

Yet the frontiers of possible galactic observation were growing dimmer by the second, for the galaxies were subsequently discovered to be rushing away from each other—some at the appalling rate of one-fifth the velocity of light. To understand this notion of the expanding universe, imagine a small boy with a can of red paint and a yellow balloon (Fig. 32). The boy blows up the balloon a little

Figure 32. The universe is expanding.

way and daubs it with a number of red spots. The spots harden immediately and if the boy continues to inflate the balloon, the paint blobs all move away from each other as the balloon stretches. Apparently this is what is happening to the galaxies in our universe.

Now it was logical to assume that, although the universe is expanding at a terrific rate, it nevertheless represents a sphere which, however fantastically huge, can be considered finite. Also, relativistic physics showed that space exists in time. Both depending on high velocities and great masses, they were proven to be variable quantities and therefore of finite extent and duration. Why then should the universe, woven of finite spacetime, be infinite?

Einstein's equations worked brilliantly in our own celestial "neighborhood," or solar system. Accordingly, as a believer in the uniformity of nature, he undertook to apply these laws to the universe as a whole. Thus, in 1917, Einstein worked out a new cosmogony by generalizing his equations of the gravitational field.

Yet it seemed, for once, that the part was not the true reflection of the whole. Einstein's first spherical and finite "model" of the universe was challenged on all sides by theory and observation.

The gravitational field or distortion of geometry around the mass of the sun becomes less at greater distances from the sun's center, yet it is still spherical. The paths of the receding galaxies, however, do not appear to follow a curve closing back on itself, but rather a straight line always leading farther and farther away. Also, the velocity of their motion *grows* with the distance. It became clear therefore that the dynamics and geometry of the universe as a whole cannot be a simple generalization of a "local" gravitational situation as exemplified by our own solar system.

Now a sphere, regardless of how huge it may be, is a *finite* concept. On the other hand, a path of motion which does not come to an end, as in the case of the receding galaxies, is an *infinite* idea. Is our universe, then, finite like a sphere or infinite like a line? This was the dilemma in which Einstein eventually found himself.

Men of ancient times believed in a finite world, largely because they could not imagine infiniteness. Newton's mechanics gave a realistic interpretation of this concept by saying that space itself is infinite, while the agglomeration of stars within it is a finite system. Yet light rays were supposed to travel in straight lines; consequently, light should be carried away from the stellar sources emitting it. Theoretically, then, the island universe of stars should become successively darker and outer space successively brighter. Also, all the finite matter of stars, as it becomes emitted in radiant form, should finally disappear into the infinite void of outer space. Observation, however, appeared to indicate that the light of distant space is actually fainter than that in the vicinity of stars.

When Einstein demonstrated the bending of light and space around matter, the distressing thought of never-to-be-returned light vanished. If light follows a curved path, a situation may arise in which this curve will again "double back" on itself and light will arrive back at its source, just as our two-dimensional beings did when their world was glued together. Also, the individual space curvatures would form great spheres which close back on themselves; hence, the entire universe could be considered as closed and finite.

This curvature, as a whole, depends on matter; if we know the material content of the universe we may calculate its size. The average density of matter in the universe was established, after painstaking "sample" observations, by Edwin P. Hubble and his co-workers at Mt. Wilson Observatory. It was found to be approximately in the ratio of a hydrogen atom occupying a container of "space" measuring 1.3 cubic yards.

Einstein used this figure in his field equations and saw that it yielded a positive quantity, or positive curvature. Following this, his original model of the universe was like the upper surface of our Plexiglas backgammon board, that is, a Riemannian geometry, and further resembled the spherical "local" gravitational field produced by the mass of the sun. As a result of his calculations, Einstein startled the world by stating that the diameter of the universe was some 70 billion light years—a fantastically huge figure, yet finite nevertheless!

The Newtonian universe of stars was supposed to be held in equilibrium by gravitational and inertial forces. Einstein, in order to balance gravitational attraction, introduced a new constant—that of *gravitational repulsion*.

As the opposite of gravitational force, this quantity had to have the peculiar nature of increasing as the distance increased—which is not in accordance with the general behavior of forces. This universe in equilibrium had to be immobile from the point of view of time. If it were not, one could suppose that just as a traveler in space would eventually return to his starting point, time too would return; and thus, after an immense but finite time interval, all events would happen again, and human history would repeat itself. Were the time axis curved like space axes, Columbus would again discover America; the Civil War would rage again; we ourselves would be re-born. Again and again we would repeat every little mistake, like taking the uptown bus instead of the downtown one. Luckily, however, this

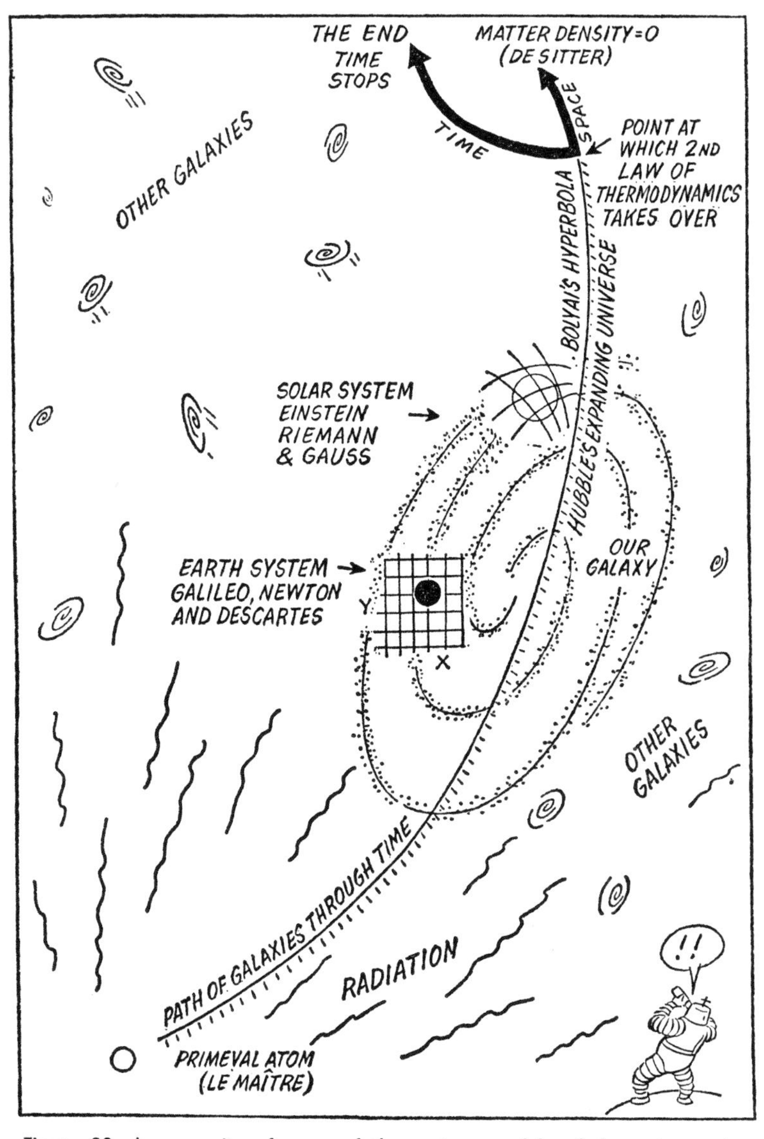

Figure 33. A composite of some of the various models of the universe (not proportional).

is futile speculation because, in the cosmic version of the four-dimensional coordinate, the time axis remains straight.

In another model of a finite and static universe (Fig. 33), the Dutch mathematician de Sitter proposed that space and time were both curved, somewhat in the form of a globe, with the latitude being time and the longitude being the space coordinate. In such a universe, matter is so dispersed in space that it has no appreciable influence.

Einstein's field equations, however, permitted other, non-static, dynamic solutions if certain corrections were made. In 1920, Alexander Friedmann, a Russian mathematician, constructed two "moving" models of universes, one of which contracts with time while the other expands. One presents positive curvature, as does Einstein's. It is in following ellipses that galaxies recede from one another. They then turn back after reaching a maximum distance. Arriving eventually at a minimum distance, their contraction ceases and their expansion again begins and so on.

In the other model, the universe starts from a very contracted state and expands following a hyperbolic path. Now hyperbolas, in marking growing distances, also produce negative curvatures, as in the inside portion of our Plexiglas backgammon board. This implies Bolyaian geometry and points toward an infinite universe where neither time nor space will meet each other again.

Then Georges Lemaître, a Belgian scientist, developed the idea of an expanding universe by presupposing a homogeneous "primeval atom" which was highly compressed and very hot. Once having begun its expansion it has grown in volume ever since.

Theoretical support for this theory came from Sir Arthur Eddington who showed how Einstein's static model, which is basically "unstable," expands when moved from its equilibrium. Crucial proof of such motion came in 1929, when Edwin Hubble's experiments demonstrated that the galaxies are rushing away from each other with ever-increasing escape velocity.

Hubble also observed that the light which reaches us from other galaxies is shifted toward the red end of the spectrum, a sign that they are becoming gradually fainter. This must mean that their distance from us is increasing at a rapid rate. According to the velocity-distance relationship, their velocity was measured and found to be of such magnitude that, when compared to the motion of individual gravitational systems, it is like comparing the speed of a turtle with that of a jet plane.

From the distances and velocities involved in this galactic recession, the starting time of their flights could be calculated. In this way, it was also possible to calculate the actual age of our universe. Astronomers now believe that it must be about five billion years old. For a time, due to errors in these calculations, this birthday was believed to have occurred only two billion years ago; this, however, was contradicted by certain radioactive substances known positively to be three billion or more years old. This would have been strange indeed—living in a two-billion-year-old universe which contained three-billion-year-old substances!

Yet there still remained the contradictions between the laws governing the motion of galaxies and those reigning inside them in smaller gravitational systems. Let us again take advantage of our special equipment to examine them, together with the ultimate question itself: Is our universe finite in its parts, and at the same time infinite as a whole?

It is unnecessary to emphasize that such a space exploration as we propose to make is beyond human possibility. We have only to remind ourselves that the diameter of our own solar system is 10,000 light years across, and that of the Milky Way about 100,000 light years. Theoretically, we could reach the sun (if we could biologically stand the terrific heat there) by traveling at the velocity of light for 8.18 minutes; but no man could live long enough to reach a star of another galaxy, even were he a light ray itself. The journey of such a light ray from earth to the nebulae of Andromeda, for example, would take ten million years.

As we cover short distances on earth, Euclidian geometry and the straight-lined coordinates of Descartes serve us adequately. Traveling on the entire earth's surface, however, we find that Gaussian coordinates and geodetic geometry are recommended. Yet, Newtonian laws of motion are valid in the vicinity of earth and his laws of gravitation are good approximations of those holding in the entire planetary system.

As we investigate the solar system as a whole, however, we find it more advisable to shift over to Einstein's four-dimensional space-time continuum. By doing so, we see that not only the "spaceship" on which we live—old Mother Earth—is rotating, but so is its orbit. Einstein's concept of the universe thus widens the horizon of our knowledge to the limits of a large spacetime sphere where a four-dimensional graph is the only efficient guide.

This model of the universe is like the exterior of the balloon of our small boy. Traveling "outside" it for a better look we see great quantities of irregular dots representing gravitation fields and distortions of space; conglomerations of these resolve into more regular formations—galaxies. This "balloon" is a four-dimensional continuum which is finite yet boundless. If we realize that, beside the gravitational, roughly spherical motion inside the "dots," the "dots" themselves (the galaxies) perform a rapid, hyperbolic motion thus causing the increase of the volume of the entire balloon, we find ourselves inside the Friedmann-Lemaître universe.

Where are these giant galaxies hurrying? From whence did they come?

Let's try to find an answer by jumping on the t axis instead of using space coordinates alone and see what might have been happening at the beginning of time. In doing so, we enter the cosmological realm of George Gamow, the famous Russian-born American scientist. Gamow stated that there first must have been a maximum compression of everything that was to form the universe as it presently exists. Later, a relativistic expansion began where everything existed as radiation with only negligible amounts of matter here and there. For a long time this radiation "outnumbered" matter until a cooling-off process set in and more and more matter originated. Particles were united, the elements were formed and eventually human life evolved on at least one of the small planets of one of the stars. It is interesting to note that in the Gamow cosmology, the entire present chemical make-up of the universe took place in the first half hour of its existence!

With the formation of more and more matter, the weight of gravitation took over. Yet, as it did so, the nebulae and galaxies which had been formed of radiation and matter were pulled apart under the influence of a general expansion. The distance between them grew in proportion to the square root of the time at which they traveled. And their outward, never-to-return flight, as the "red shift" indicates, goes on and on.

With radiant energy and matter thus diffused far into the "space beyond space," the day may come when the density of matter will be almost zero. In this incredible emptiness, resembling the de Sitter model, space would not be measurable any more and the time axis would become static. Time would thus become timeless, for there would be no time at all.

Since we have at our disposal our Guided Tour equipment and are able to travel forward on the t axis, let us look at how the beginning of this cosmic dissolution *might* affect the earth.

It is a frightening picture which comes before us and we wonder if, this time at least, our sense of imaginative abstraction has not played tricks on us. Here is what we see:

Just as the galaxy has been speeding away from its neighboring galaxies, so has the galaxy itself been slowly breaking up. Our solar system, too, has been deteriorating following the inexorable law of expansion into a timeless void. The sun has been growing steadily dimmer. On earth, the polar caps have encroached hundreds of miles toward the equator. Scientists have been feverishly developing giant nuclear heating plants beneath the earth's surface. The population of the earth, in fact, will eventually be forced to burrow beneath the planet's crust to sustain life.

For a time, life could go on in this way. Soon, however, the earth, also obeying the cosmic laws of expansion, would be shooting outward at such a rate of speed that shrinkage would occur, life would disappear and time would slowly draw to a close.

Is there no possibility of escaping this last "day"—a day which would in fact become synonymous with the word "forever"?

There is, if we believe that once the universe reaches its maximum expansion it will again begin to contract until it reaches maximum condensation. The whole process would then begin again—expansion and contraction following each other in an everlasting action as in Friedmann's periodic model of the universe. Yet, this could only happen if there were sufficient matter left outside the galaxies to re-aggregate.

Again, there is hope in the hypothesis of continuous creation, as recently proposed by the British scientists H. Bondi, T. Gold and F. Hoyle. In their universe, matter lost by expansion is continually being recreated and the average density of matter always remains the same. Other physicists, however, are reluctant to accept this pleasant possibility, although it would eliminate the paradox which almost all other theories of the universe contain. This is the contradiction between the expanding galactic motion and the cooling off or slowing down of matter as condensation takes place.

We mentioned astronomical observations which, like the velocity-distance law, challenge this optimistic cosmogony. Now we shall turn toward purely physical facts which, alas, seem to strengthen the pessimistic arguments.

CHAPTER △ NINETEEN

MACROCOSM AND MICROCOSM

BROWNIAN MOTION

HEAT & THERMAL EQUILIBRIUM

2ND LAW OF THERMODYNAMICS

We have seen that for decades the whole range of undulatory motion—and the force fields in which electromagnetic waves travel—were not considered from the material point of view. Nevertheless, scientists had always had to reckon with some sort of *oscillator,* that is, *something* which initiated vibratory motion. As scientists use the term, an *oscillator* is simply a shorthand way of describing any agent which emits waves, whether these waves be sonic or electromagnetic.

Now the mechanical aspect of this oscillator is that of the material point which oscillates along a line and is considered to be a mass point of one single dimension, the linear one. No further physical aspect was given to this "linear oscillator." Yet its action was clearly defined in the laws of frequency which we reviewed in a previous chapter.

With the discovery of the electron, however, the situation changed somewhat. The definite turning point came when Max Planck, a German physicist, introduced the concept of *light quanta.* He stated that light, as well as all radiant energy, is emitted and absorbed by matter in small units or packets, which themselves are indivisible. Planck called this unit of radiant energy a *quantum.*

The Quantum Theory, as we shall see, is not merely a new particle theory of light. While the principle itself is new, it is not as difficult to accept as that of the Theory of Relativity. The relativity theory necessitates correction in measurements only in the realm of high velocities and great masses; the theory of quanta became the basis for nearly all study *inside* the atom.

Now the Quantum Theory was to reveal a serious gulf which apparently existed between the world of the most-small (called the *microcosm,* actually the sphere of the atom) and the large scale objects of everyday life (called the *macrocosm*). Not only stars, galaxies and the universe itself belong to the macrocosm but also the point of a pencil, we ourselves, in fact anything we can observe without the aid of a microscope. Further, if the *action* of one individual quantity of the atomic world is to be considered, it is called the *microstate;* conversely, when many quantities are involved, physicists refer to them as the *macrostate.*

Where exactly does the frontier lie between these two worlds where apparently conflicting basic laws seem to reign? Obviously somewhere in the kingdom of molecules. Molecules cannot be seen by the naked eye, yet sensitive apparatus can register their *random* and *disorderly* motion. This phenomenon is called the *Brownian motion* after its discoverer, Robert Brown, a Scottish

Figure 34. The Brownian motion as it might look applied to space travel. The spaceships represent molecules in random motion.

botanist (Fig. 34). Brown first observed this motion while studying plant spores which were large enough to be seen through a microscope yet small enough to behave like molecules. It was in this area of Brown's investigation that the bridge between small and large scale phenomena existed.

Physicists, however, had to rely mostly on calculations alone when describing this tiny world of agitating molecules. Their calculations later unveiled one of the most fascinating secrets of all physics—that the macrostate of moving molecules is the basis of the hydrogen bomb.

Molecules, you may remember, are the smallest particles of a substance—an element or a compound—which, in spite of their smallness, still remain that substance. Molecules of like substances are held together by a cohesive force called the *intermolecular force.* This is strongest in solids, weaker in liquids, and virtually non-existent in gases.

Let us review a few basic laws at this point. That forces in liquids and gases behave differently from those in solid bodies was one of the first recognitions in the study of physics. We all remember Archimedes' Law: that objects submerged in fluids are buoyed up by a force equal to the weight of the gas or liquid displaced. You may also have heard of the "hydrostatic paradox" solved by Pascal when he stated that confined liquids or gases transmit pressure equally everywhere inside their containers. Also, the fact that water cannot be pumped over a certain level was attributed to nature's "abhorrence of a vacuum" until Pascal discovered that it was the weight of the air, or the atmospheric pressure, which prevented the water from rising. The principle of Bernouilli completes our short review of basic physical laws, namely, that in areas where the speed of fluids increases, the pressure exerted decreases, and vice-versa.

Now the opposing phenomenon that counteracts *cohesion* among molecules is *heat,* which breaks down intermolecular forces and causes molecules to expand. Ice, for example, sufficiently heated, melts into water; hot water in turn expands into vapor when sufficiently heated. If *temperature* (the degree of hotness) becomes sufficiently low, intermolecular forces become stronger than thermal ones; molecules are then cemented together into regular geometrical patterns or crystalline forms, like ice crystals. Heat has its best chance of "cracking" intermolecular force when molecules are loosely associated, as in gases. When molecules are thus "chased" by heat they are said to be in *thermal* motion.

Inside our sun, gases are perpetually burning. It has been established that the intense radiation produced there is not caused by ordinary radioactivity but is the effect of fantastically high temperatures which keep molecules there in ceaseless motion. Temperatures inside the sun have been estimated at 14 to 20 million degrees centigrade. Particles in such hot systems collide incessantly with each other and the energy thus produced is practically inexhaustible.

When it was established that this so-called *thermonuclear reaction* in the sun is the transformation of hydrogen into helium (plus radiant energy), it became natural to consider the production of artificial thermonuclear energy by man. Now the burning of hydrogen here is not ordinary combustion; besides, hydrogen nuclei "burn" too slowly for artificial purposes. Therefore, the hydrogen isotope known as "heavy water," obtained by electrolytic procedures, is used. But this isotope of hydrogen, known as *deuterium,* is not produced directly by simple electrolysis; it also exists in nature. Edward Teller, the Hungarian-born American and (together with others) "Father of the Hydrogen Bomb" considered another isotope, *tritium,* which can only be produced artificially.

At present, thermonuclear energy production is not as advanced as atomic energy production. The reason is twofold. While the gases used must be sufficiently rarefied in order not to explode due to the pressure exerted against the walls enclosing them, they must, at the same time, be kept at a distance from these walls. Otherwise the gases would lose their precious temperature. This necessary distance can be maintained by a protective magnetic field where electrically charged particles encounter a force perpendicular to their direction. As the deuterium gas is ionized, negative electrons and positive nuclei, called *deuterons,* are formed and kept away from the walls. If this process is entirely successful, particles that collide will not explode, and controlled, thermonuclear energy will be produced. To achieve this a vast amount of heat is needed.

What exactly *is* heat which, if present in amounts high enough, is capable of producing nuclear reactions more intense than those of radioactive decay?

Heat, for a long time, was thought to be a substance in itself. Count Rumford, an American-born British physicist, began to wonder how it was possible that when cannons were bored, large amounts of heat were produced yet no additional "substance" was added. Only *work* was added, he reasoned, and therefore only this mechanical work could have produced the heat. Mechanical work is energy produced, in one form or another, by motion, and is called *kinetic* energy. Later, James Joule successfully transformed mechanical energy into heat. His experiment proved that heat is the kinetic energy bodies possess when their molecules are in *thermal motion.*

With the increase of temperature, the thermal motion of molecules also increases, just as dancers are more animated in a heated ballroom than in a cold one. Yet, just as stout dancers move more slowly than slender ones, heavier molecules in a compound "dance" more slowly than lighter ones. When you observe a great number of dancers together from a very high balcony, you may be so far away from them that you are unable to tell which are dancing fast and which slow. All that you actually see is a bunch of tiny specks which, as a whole, move and fluctuate as one rubbery body. In the same way, a physicist observing many moving molecules together may notice that the *sum* of their kinetic energy remains always the same. This law is called the *equipartition of energies* and describes the behavior of a great many molecules moving together in thermal motion—that is, considering them from the viewpoint of the macrostate.

Thus the *average* energy could be established for a *group* of molecules without bothering with the individual behavior of each molecule. All the experimenter has to do is to collect as many data as possible. This statistical method was used when Maxwell presented the mathematical abstraction for this law.

Heat that is put to work is energy in transformation. Hermann Helmholtz, a German physicist, observed that the total amount of heat and work energies remain always the same. This is so because energies can transform into each other but can never be created or destroyed. This is the principle of Conservation of Energy which we encountered in a previous chapter. Here we may simply add that it is also the First Law of Thermodynamics.

In steam engines, heat transforms into mechanical energy. Sadi Carnot, a French engineer, together with Lord Kelvin, established that not all heat energy transforms by itself. Heat transformation, or heat-flow, has the unique property that it can travel, without assistance from an outside agent, in one direction only—from hot toward cold. Its course is irreversible. This phenomenon is the Second Law of Thermodynamics. And it is one of the most frightening of all the laws in nature. Why?

Say we have two adjoining rooms, only one of which—the living

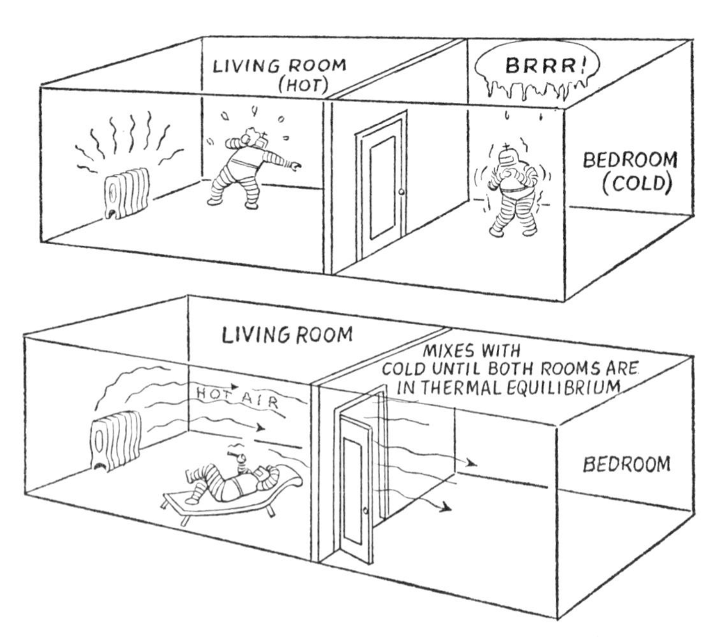

Figure 35. Warm air always flows to a cooler place until thermal equilibrium is reached.

room—is heated (Fig. 35). In order to pass some of the heat into an unheated bedroom, we open the door between them. Soon hot and cold air mingle until both rooms attain the same temperature; the living room is less hot than before, and the bedroom is not as cold as before. Our two rooms are now said to be in *thermal equilibrium.* If we wished to reverse the process and again get our living room as hot as it was before we opened the door, we would find that this cannot be done without extra work! The heat which flowed from the hot room into the cooler room is no longer available. There is as much heat energy present in the two rooms as there was alone in the living room before, but it has now become dissipated and cannot ever be recaptured. As an index of the magnitude of non-available heat, physicists use the term *entropy,* which determines quantitatively the amount of this non-availability. Since heat flows only from hot to cold, this amount, or entropy, can increase but never decrease in a system. We saw that when mechanical energy was transformed into heat energy, molecules of the heated system became more and more excited, that is, their crystalline order changed into disorder. Therefore, we may also say that entropy shows the degree of disorder among molecules; the greater the degree of disorder, the higher the entropy.

When we studied the spectrum we learned that heat was recognized to be radiant, invisible energy, having wavelengths longer than those which our eye is capable of seeing. Heated bodies, however, can emit not only these infrared waves, but also visible ones if such bodies are sufficiently heated. If we forget and leave our toaster on, the red radiation of its filaments soon becomes more and more bluish; indeed, if the filaments could hold up under sufficient temperatures they could illuminate an entire room. This leads us, then, to Wien's law—namely, that the hotter a body is, the shorter the emitted radiation's wavelength. Wien, together with Stefan and Boltzmann, further observed that the total intensity of the radiation emitted by such a hot body is exactly equal to its temperature raised to the fourth power:

Temperature^4 = radiation. Or, to be exact:

PT^4 = radiation, where P equals the proportionality constant.

Boltzmann also explained that the irreversibility of heat-flow is an equalization process. In our two rooms, hotter and cooler air tended to be equalized; and so do fast moving molecules in a system tend to equalize their energy with that of slower molecules. Fast molecules are in a state of radiation; slow molecules are in a state of matter. Obviously, then, matter and radiation thus mixed possess different velocities. When molecules collide it can happen that a slow or "matter-molecule" loses its small amount of velocity, at the same time imparting greater velocity to a fast "radiant-molecule." Yet this seldom happens and does not influence the total velocity or radiant energy of the entire system. In fact, the reverse happens much more often, so that actually the average velocity of the entire system decreases or "cools off," until thermal equilibrium is established.

Since the individual velocities of molecules are different in a given body, only their *average* can be considered as the degree of heat in that body. To establish this average, Boltzmann, like Maxwell, used statistical means, much as a TV program's "rating" is determined by sampling the listening public's frequency in tuning it in.

Thus the Second Law of Thermodynamics became the first *statistical* law in physics to take the place of an absolutely rigid one. It opened the door to the realm of probabilities which has worked amazingly well for science ever since. Science, however, paid a high price for this; it was forced to admit that the greatest exactitude it could ever hope to attain in certain realms is, at best, only an approximation.

Its purely statistical aspect, however, did not serve to change the frightening implications of the Second Law of Thermodynamics. Because heat moves only in one direction—because nature's course is in effect a "river of no return"—because entropy is steadily marching toward its maximum—all these things strongly suggest that the conservation of matter and energy cannot go on forever. If this is true, then the fate of the universe is sealed, for everything which exists is progressing toward a very distant yet irrevocable end. That is, all heat in the universe is slowly yet inexorably dissipating itself into a vast thermal equilibrium or cosmic coolness. Hence, the sun, together with all hot celestial bodies, is gradually burning itself out and yielding up precious and irreplaceable radiation. In this inherent property of heat apparently lies the dim day of doom threatening the universe. Indeed, unless another Prometheus bearing the priceless gift of fire to mankind reappears on the scene, the universe we know may end in a vast and timeless chilliness. Thus the Second Law of Thermodynamics suggests a tale as tragic as that of the expansion of the universe.

Yet, could not energy and matter and all that now exists—even if destroyed—once again be recreated? Indeed, the Second Law of Thermodynamics considers things only from the point of view of the macrostate—or the behavior of many molecules. But how about the microstate—or individual molecules? The motions of material particles, we learned, are events not irreversible but *reversible.* Many particles or oscillators in the electromagnetic field are described in their macrostate, which may be an eternal wandering from hot to cooler in terms of thermodynamics. But in the oscillation of one-dimensional or linear motion of a single oscillator in the microstate, we may perhaps find sanctuary from the Second Law of Thermodynamics.

And Planck, who found the smallest quantity of radiant energy—called so rightfully the *element of action*—was concerned only with this microstate. Let us see whether this viewpoint is not more optimistic than that drawn by the apocalyptic law of heat.

CHAPTER △ TWENTY

QUANTUM THEORY

BLACK BODIES, CAVITIES & "JEANS' CUBE"

PLANCK'S CONSTANT *h*

EINSTEIN'S PHOTOELECTRIC EFFECT

The contradiction between the macrostate and the microstate became obvious when energy distribution in a so-called "black body" and the energy distribution in a so-called "cavity" were compared.

Physicists call a perfect light-absorber a "black body." As is well known, the best absorbers of light are also the best emitters of it, and such a black body would thus be a perfect emitter. Every girl knows that she is better protected against the sun in a white hat than in a black one because black absorbs light while white reflects most of it.

There are no perfect light-absorbing and light-emitting "black bodies" in nature, and no perfectly isolated "cavities," or systems in thermal equilibrium, either. Both are ideal systems created theoretically for the purpose of demonstration.

The spectrum emitted by a black body was found, theoretically, to be identical with the spectral distribution of energy inside a cavity (Fig. 36). Therefore, classical physics suggested that the *intensity* of radiant energies should also grow in the case of black bodies with the growing of velocities, just as total energy grows in the cavity when it is heated.

Yet were the intensity of radiant energies to increase infinitely, all energies would concentrate in the realm of very short wave-lengths. This would go on and on because, theoretically, there is no wavelength so short that it could not be even shorter. Apparently,

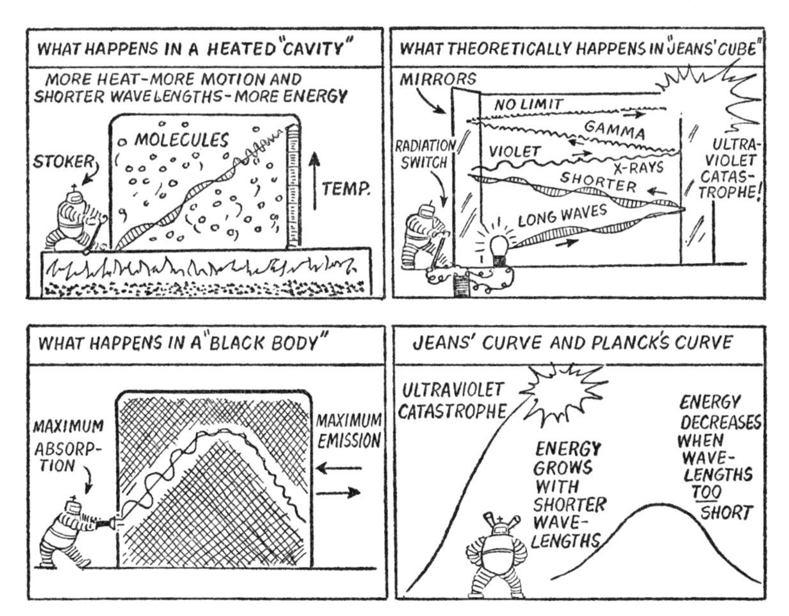

Figure 36. The "ultraviolet catastrophe"—a paradox which led to the birth of Planck's Quantum Theory.

however, the growing of energy intensity has a limit. It grows for a while, together with the shortening of wavelengths, but then it simply does not grow any more.

This became clear when Sir James Jeans, a British physicist, constructed a hypothetical "cube," with walls made of mirrors which would reflect perfectly all radiation "enclosed" in this cube. Within the cube, theoretically, energy intensities would grow until the whole system would be destroyed by the powerful ultraviolet energies produced. In reality, however, energy intensities cannot grow *ad infinitum* and all radiant energy does not turn into ultraviolet energy in split seconds; hence, no "ultraviolet catastrophe" actually occurs in nature.

The reason for the discrepancy between black bodies and cavities, Planck reasoned, is that the heated molecules in the cavity, though very numerous, are still of a finite number, and thus the distribution of finite energy intensities is possible among them—

whereas the wavelengths which black bodies theoretically emit are infinite.

Apparently nature does not always follow the classical law valid for heated bodies. As we cannot change nature, Planck went on, we must change the law. He proposed that, instead of thinking of radiation as a phenomenon of pure waves which can be shortened indefinitely, we consider radiations to be put together of finite quantities. This reasoning became the basis of the theory of quanta.

The law of equipartition of energies and the thermal motion of molecules constitutes the macrostate, which gives the total energy of a system, Planck stated; the motion of one single linear oscillator, producing waves of radiation, constitutes the microstate. Energy produced by oscillation does not flow as water seems to stream from the nozzle of a hose, but propagates in "doses" like medicine from a dropper (Fig. 37). The interaction between energy and matter, or the emission and the absorption of energy by matter, occurs in "jumps" and is restricted to definite quanta. Thus every

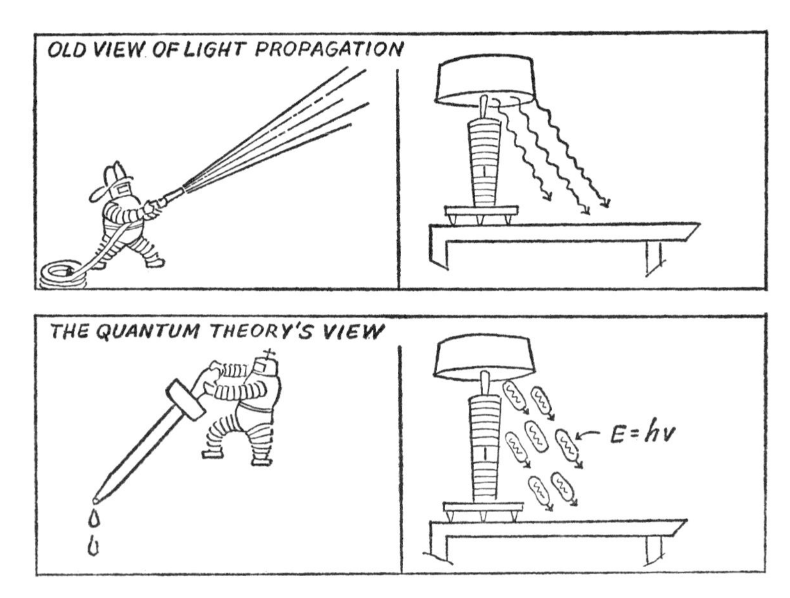

Figure 37. The classical view (above) of light propagating as continuous waves from its source. New view (below) of light as individual "quanta."

oscillator has a discrete energy value (if it has a single distinct frequency) which it can lose or gain, but no intermediary between any two levels can exist. The situation could also be likened to a "grocer" selling light and other radiant energies (as well as his other products); he can, if he wishes, sell half an apple by cutting one in two, but there is no cutting the elementary quantum of radiation into two half-quanta. The grocer could only "sell" quanta in ones, twos, threes or any integer multiplier.

All quanta of a single frequency (or, loosely speaking, color) are identical and possess the same amounts of energy. Planck discovered this irreducible quantity of light by following the statistical methods of Maxwell and Boltzmann. He divided the total energy obtained of an entire radiant system into a large but finite number of identical energy elements which were not further divisible. Planck thus showed the definite connection between frequency and energy of a light quantum by proving that the amount of energy of a light quantum is directly proportional to the number of its oscillations in a certain time. This coefficient of proportionality, which physicists call h or *Planck's constant,* is always the same. It always has the same value equal to

$$6.624 \times 10^{-27} \text{ erg./sec. or}$$
$$.000{,}000{,}000{,}000{,}000{,}000{,}000{,}000{,}006{,}624$$

In spite of its smallness, h is one of the most important constant values in nature. It establishes the link between energy and frequency. The value of the energy of light quanta is the product of h, the coefficient of proportionality, and the vibrations per second, v. Thus:

$$E \text{ (energy of light quanta)} = h \times v$$

A linear oscillator that vibrates with high velocity in the electromagnetic field cannot "handle" any other value than $h \times v$ or its integer multiple; it is restricted to these "quantized" values. Thus we see why the "ultraviolet catastrophe" of Jeans' Cube could not happen in reality; an infinite frequency means infinite energy.

The h is not actually an atomistic part of light but its *element of action;* that is, not the smallest material point or particle that oscillates, but the *action* or *effect* of the particle's oscillation.

Yet, Planck's constant h had something in common with the Newtonian particle in that it too did not fit into the field of electromagnetic waves. Not merely electrodynamics but also many other classical laws of mechanics were challenged by the Quantum Theory. The fact that only integer quanta are allowed meant a distinction between "allowed and non-allowed" values. Therefore, a new mechanics combining *quantum* and *wave mechanics* had to be created. Again, the theories of matter and motion had to be reconciled.

The first step toward this synthesis was made by Einstein, whose entire life-work was a heroic struggle toward the presentation of that harmony in nature in which he so firmly believed. His derivation of the Planck formula considers, instead of electromagnetic vibrations, the definite oscillation of particles.

Einstein thus interpreted the very words of his friend, Max Planck, who stated in 1899 that: "Bodies and waves together—and only together—present the two existing phenomena of atoms and their radiation."

Einstein applied Planck's formula when he successfully explained the so-called *photoelectric effect* which had caused his contemporaries many headaches.

Photoelectricity is the emission of free electrons by a metal when exposed to radiation (Fig. 38). No emission at all occurs, however, until the radiation exceeds a certain *frequency* value known as the *threshold frequency.* After this point, the more intensive the rays become the more electrons are emitted.

Yet intensity of the *radiation* increases only the *number* but not the *velocity* of the emitted electrons. This is in contradiction to the wave theory which says that velocity, too, should increase, much as powerful ocean waves can toss foam higher than weaker ones. The old Newtonian particle theory of light offered an analogy by saying that the strength of the light source influences the number of particles but leaves their speed unaltered.

However, if this hypothesis were true in the case of emission of free electrons, an ever-growing number of electrons should appear with increased intensity. Each would then have a different velocity. This is not so, however, since experience shows that the number and variation of velocities of the electrons are limited.

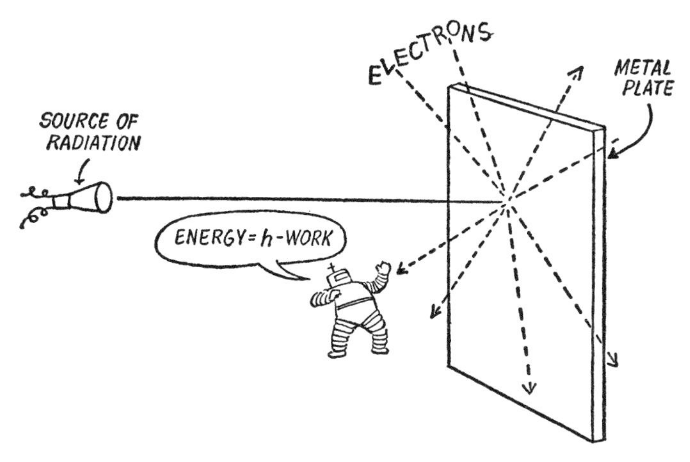

Figure 38. The photoelectric effect.

If we go along with Planck, Einstein reasoned, and admit that radiation is emitted in definite quanta, the whole process is explained. All quanta of radiation of a given frequency possess the same amount of energy. When such a quantum of radiation encounters an electron, the electron absorbs all of this energy or none of it. The amount of energy thus received by the electron from the quantum of light should be the total energy of this quantum; yet it is less. This, however, is merely because of the work the electron must use to overcome the resisting surface of the metal. Einstein stated that the energy of the electron is equal to the energy of the light quantum minus the work-energy the electron loses while leaving the metallic surface.

Arthur Compton, an American scientist, visualized the escape of an electron from the nucleus of the atom—to which it is bound by attractive forces—to be similar to that of a free electron if the energy quanta it encounters have enough energy. If the energy quanta are overwhelmingly strong, the fact that the electron was bound to the atomic system makes no difference, and its behavior becomes that of a free electron. By showing that the wavelength became longer, Compton demonstrated a loss of weight after the collision.

CHAPTER △ TWENTY-ONE

ELECTRONS—IN AND OUT OF ORBIT

QUANTUM MECHANICS

PAULI'S EXCLUSION PRINCIPLE

DE BROGLIE'S "PILOT WAVES"

SCHRÖDINGER'S WAVE EQUATION

With the explanation of the photoelectric effect it was proved that not only does the emission and absorption of light occur in separate quanta but that it is also quantized during propagation. Yet the connection between these smallest parts of radiant energy and the smallest known parts of matter—atomic particles—was not at first self-evident. The reason was largely that, while these energies were considered to travel in the form of waves, the motion of material particles was for a long time described from a classically mechanical viewpoint. Electrons were supposed to rotate about their atomic nuclei as planets do around the sun—that is, in a kind of miniature solar system.

The planetary hypothesis of the atom was first proposed in 1904, but was not accepted until Rutherford published his famous paper based on his experiments. Niels Bohr, a young Danish physicist, then began to construct a theory that would agree with Rutherford's findings—namely, the first physical picture of the so-called "nuclear atom." During his work, however, he began to question the planetary picture of the atom. The planets themselves are electrically neutral and are kept in their orbits by the balance of gravitational and centrifugal forces. Yet how can this same situation exist inside the atom where the atomic "planets"—the electrons—possess electrical charges?

When a charged particle revolves, it emits electromagnetic waves and loses a corresponding amount of energy. Now rotating electrons should, with decreasing energy, come closer and closer to the nucleus because, although their kinetic energy increases as their orbit becomes smaller, their potential energy decreases twice as fast. Thus, by all logic, they should be doomed to fall into the nucleus and, as a consequence, atomic systems could only exist for split seconds!

But we know that atomic systems exist for considerably longer periods. The suicidal jump of electrons into the nucleus never actually occurs. Why?

Obviously, said Bohr, because classical rules do not hold for the behavior of electrons. Electrons, he stated, cannot rotate in just any orbit, but only in a few of many possible ones. There they do not emit energy at all, being in a kind of balanced state. Electrons emit energy only when they change orbit—that is, jump from one of the higher "permitted" orbits to a lower one. The amount of energy thus emitted is always an integer equal to h, or a whole-number multiple of that value.

The amount of energy a hydrogen electron emits while jumping from one to another of its three orbits (Bohr stated only three were possible for electrons of hydrogen atoms) was established experimentally long before by "reading" such information in that element's spectral lines. As early as 1885, J. J. Balmer, a Swiss physicist, discovered a simple formula for the energy emission he observed while studying hydrogen atoms. The action his formula described was then determined by Bohr as the "jump" to the second orbit of the hydrogen electron. Balmer found that the frequencies presented by the spectral lines are proportional to the difference between the inverse square of 2 (that is, ¼), 3, 4, and 5, all variable integer quantities.

Later, lines corresponding to the "first jump" of the hydrogen electron were found among the wavelengths *shorter* than light, and those expressing the "third jump" among wavelengths *longer* than the visible spectra. These effects were established by Lyman and Paschen, respectively. Yet no one could explain why the hydrogen spectrum showed these lines until Bohr asserted that this is so because electron radiations are, just as light, "quantized." That is, when jumping from one orbit to another, they emit not indiscriminate amounts of radiation, but only whole-number *h* quantities, never fractions.

Now the introduction of the *h,* or *element of action,* into the world of the atom emphasized that, again, two elementary aspects of phenomena must be considered: matter and motion. Almost all the mass of matter is concentrated in the atomic nucleus, and its behavior is determined by the Theory of Special Relativity and by nuclear laws of which we shall learn in our next chapter. But nearly all material considerations may be disregarded when electrons are dealt with, for their mass is negligible; it is their motion that counts. The laws of this motion are presented by *quantum mechanics.*

These new dynamics of the microcosmos were developed within a short period. Bohr discovered that the inner orbit of hydrogen electrons was circular; later, a German physicist, Sommerfeld, proved that the two remaining orbits were elliptical, as are all other orbits of more complicated atoms. He also proved that these orbits have a definite orientation in space. By establishing the requirements space must satisfy to be adequate for electron orbits, he "quantized" space too.

What orders these quantum conditions? Why do electrons of more complicated atoms with many electrons not all land finally in the lowest orbit when jumping from higher to lower orbits?

This, stated the late W. Pauli, a Swiss physicist, is because there is simply no place for them there! Only two electrons can co-exist in one orbit, each "spinning" about their axes in opposite directions. If there are more than two of them, as in the case of atoms of higher atomic number, new orbits must be created for them. Just as a household requires more cabinets for household objects as time goes by, so atoms possessing many electrons need more atomic "cabinets," or atomic shells. Likewise, atoms missing a few electrons from their shells may complete them by "stealing" electrons from the shells of other atoms—but only if these themselves are in nearly empty shells. Those elements which possess but a few electrons in their outer shells yield them willingly, much as we are apt to throw away nearly empty packs of matches. In this way, various elements form compounds, and the laws of chemical valency, discussed in a previous chapter, gain a logical basis for their existence. This phenomenon is known as the *Pauli Exclusion Principle.*

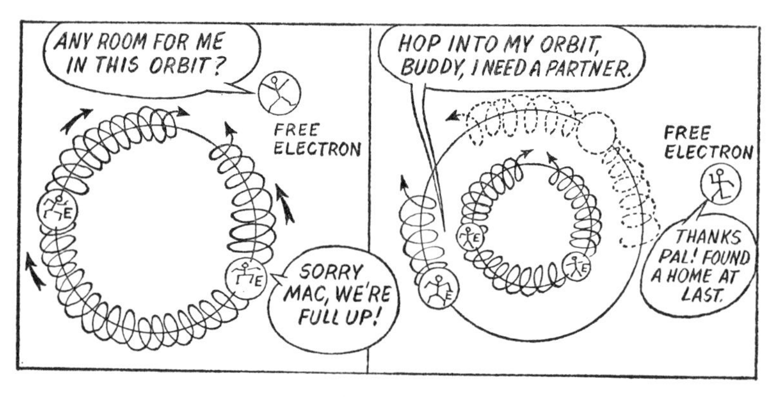

Figure 39. The Exclusion Principle.

While the quanta laws of Pauli, Sommerfeld and Bohr thus solved many long-standing physical riddles, they also created new ones. The most puzzling among them was the way in which electrons seemed to "choose" their orbits. How could electrons "know" that there is no room for them in a certain orbit? Or were they, as the French physicist Louis de Broglie suspected, *guided* by something?

When de Broglie introduced the hypothesis of a "pilot wave" accompanying each electron in its orbital flight, he assumed just that. He came to this conclusion by remembering the analogy (established by Fermat as early as the 17th century) between the least possible "action" (taken in the technical sense) a particle performs in any mechanical system, and the path followed by a light ray which covers a distance in a minimum or maximum time in an optical system.

This comparison, however, appeared to be artificial because of the difference which exists between the velocity of mechanical particles and the "phase" velocity in optical systems—phases being stages in the advancement of waves. But if, instead of phase-velocity, *group-velocity* is considered, the situation becomes different. If the group-velocity—the velocity at which signals propagate—is taken, de Broglie asserted, the velocity of waves becomes identical with the velocity of particles, *if* the value of the wavelength is a light quanta divided by mass and velocity. This *de Broglie wavelength* should thus be that of the "pilot wave" accompanying the electron in its orbit. It would go round and round there, functioning as a "standing" wave, much as those produced by stringed instruments. The quantum orbit conditions would then be reduced to the simple requirement of whole-number wavelengths necessary to complete the circle. And the electron, instead of "knowing" which orbit it "chooses" to take, would depend on the de Broglie pilot-wave ratio:

$$\frac{h}{mv}$$

or, quanta per *m*ass and *v*elocity.

If, reasoned Einstein, de Broglie is correct and electrons indeed appear in the company of waves, then freely flying electrons should also exhibit diffraction and other common wave effects.

The diffraction of X-rays had already been demonstrated by using crystal spectrographs. When C. J. Davisson and L. H. Germer, American scientists, passed through this crystal an accelerated beam of electrons, the result produced the anticipated diffraction. And the value of this wavelength was that predicted by de Broglie.

If mechanical particles are so closely associated with wave motion, there must be a mechanics which treats them as such phenomena. This *wave* or *quantum mechanics* would be in the same relation to ordinary, large-scale mechanics as physical optics is to geometrical optics. Such was the theory of E. Schrödinger, a brilliant Austrian physicist.

Geometrical optics deals exclusively with the reflective aspects of light. It is the field in which light is treated as rays traveling in a given medium in straight lines. It does not consider other physical properties of light. This is the task of physical optics.

Schrödinger stated that as geometrical optics does not "understand" diffraction (one of the physical properties of light) so are ordinary "macrostate" mechanics unable adequately to deal with "microstate" motions when particles of tiny magnitudes and waves are considered individually.

We have seen that any wave motion can be described mathematically by a differential equation. In such an equation Schrödinger inserted the de Broglie wavelength, which is a quantized phenomenon. Now if differential equations were created to describe continuous actions, how could a quantized, or discrete, concept fit into them?

That Schrödinger was nevertheless able to accomplish this was a salute to his mathematical genius. His solution of the wave equation "worked" and became the mathematical foundation of the whole world of individual quanta. It generalized the idea originated by Bohr for any mechanical problem of electrons outside the nucleus of the atom.

Schrödinger succeeded in this by sheer mathematical wizardry. He met quantum conditions *and* the requirements of continuity by focusing his attention only on solutions which were physically admissible and on characteristic functions of wave mechanics. Just as law-makers often create laws by legalizing generally accepted customs, Schrödinger presented quantized *and* continuous concepts together, because *together* they described motion in the world of the Exceedingly Small. In the world of the smaller yet, however, the so-called *quantum electrodynamics* must replace Schrödinger's simpler quantum mechanics.

Schrödinger's mechanics is comparatively simple if it deals with a single-valued, one-dimensional linear oscillator, or individual electrons with the definite energy which quantum principles require. Yet if more electrons, such as we find in a molecule, for example, are studied, they must be considered where they actually have their being—that is, in three-dimensional space. With the addition of this aspect, called *extra freedom,* the mathematical presentation became more complex.

When more complex cases are treated in which time and indefinite energies must be considered, they can only be presented by many-dimensional *superspaces.* In dealing with these superspaces in a previous chapter, we saw that we had great difficulty in imagining them with our limited senses. Likewise, we cannot present in any pictorial way the rotations of electrons not confined to a plane, but occurring in three- or more-dimensional space.

Guided by such considerations, Werner Heisenberg, some time before Schrödinger's wave equation was published, presented a formal method which was free from all physical "appearances." If we cannot use large-scale measuring methods to define time and space within the atom, Heisenberg claimed, we must consider them as a set of unspecified quantities and operate with them in a form without definite numerical value. His so-called *matrices* yield good results but are generally less convenient than are actual equations because they deliberately avoid using real physical values.

However, it became clear that the physical values of time and space were not only different concepts in the atomic world (microcosmos) and the large-scale world (macrocosmos), but they were also impossible to measure precisely together. Heisenberg demonstrated this in his *uncertainty principle,* which became a philosophical cornerstone in the world of Tiniest Quantities.

CHAPTER △ TWENTY-TWO

THE PRINCIPLE OF UNCERTAINTY

MOMENTUM & POSITION

THE "TUNNEL EFFECT"

A NUCLEAR "ALCATRAZ"

NEUTRONS, MESONS & NEUTRINOS

The *Uncertainty Principle,* as set forth by Heisenberg, indicates that our ability to observe physical phenomena is limited. We arrive at such limits when we accurately try to describe one individual particle from all aspects in the World of the Most Small.

The most evident reason why we cannot satisfactorily accomplish this is because of the disturbances caused by the measuring instruments themselves. The smaller the object to be measured, the more significant these disturbances become. Ultimately they alter the very data we wish to establish.

Housewives of a few decades ago often encountered similar "disturbances" caused by certain measuring "gauges." In those days sour cream, for example, was not sold in the familiar containers of today. Women had to carry their own one-pint cans to the markets where the cream was ladled out by the shopkeeper. Many housewives, however, felt cheated when the shopkeeper grossly plunged his ladle into the cans and left it there during the measuring process. Because the volume of the ladle elevated the level of the cream, the one-pint can looked filled before it actually was. Thus, in a crude sense, the "instrument" affected the "data."

This illustration will perhaps help us to understand how measuring instruments influence the results when data are sought on such delicate phenomena as electrons. When an entire beam of electrons is passed through a narrow, though sufficiently long, slit, the "wave packets" pass readily through (Fig. 40). The motion of the particles is determined by wave mechanics, and corresponding diffraction occurs. It is at this point that microstate and macrostate meet. Physicists say that the phenomenon is large enough to expect diffraction as determined by wave mechanics—diffraction being the deflection observed when radiation passes through the slit.

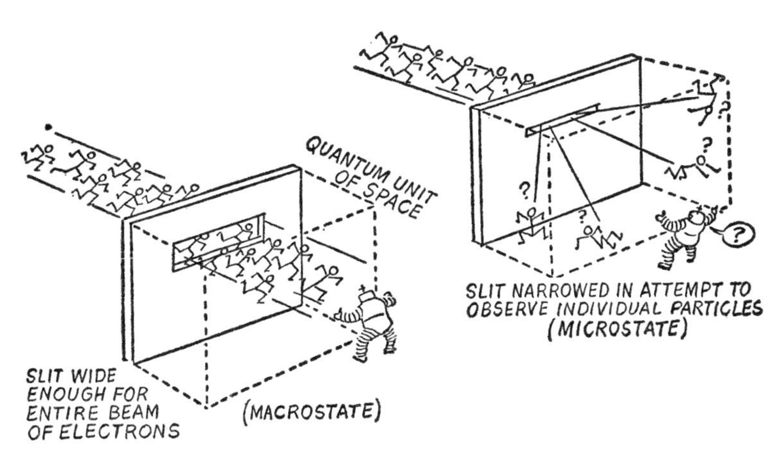

Figure 40. The point at which *macrostate* and *microstate* meet, showing the Uncertainty Principle.

Yet when we narrow the slit further in the hope of observing individual particles we also limit the wavelength, and the wave will then spread too widely on account of diffraction. Thus, when we try to observe the individual particles that went through the opening we simply cannot find them. Certainly they are somewhere within the wave packet, but in what part of it? Phases of waves occur in units, each of which is "worth" a quantum—that is, having the value of Planck's constant, h. And, since these are the smallest units possible, the best we can do is to assign the position of the electron we are dealing with to one of these quantized packets. To which one? Probably to the one in which the energy density is largest.

Yet, the energy of our particle is quantized, too! Therefore, any data concerning the energy amount "downwards" of this elementary quantum are also uncertain. In addition, to focus our attention correctly on the position of the particle we must not forget that a certain time interval is needed. Knowing the relation between time and frequency, we must not be astonished that this definite time interval affects the frequency range, inasmuch as it broadens the spectral lines to the extent that we are not really able to perceive the original situation we wished to observe. On the contrary, we merely witness the disturbance *caused* by the *very act* of observing!

This then is the fundamental meaning of the Uncertainty Principle. But Heisenberg, its author, was far from saying that all observation was consequently futile. Instead, he furnished a useful tool for cutting down the uncertainty to a minimum by finding the exact relationship between the limiting uncertainty of position and the uncertainty of momentum of the measured particle. The expressions *momentum* and *position,* as used in the microworld, carry a distinctly different meaning than they do in the macroworld, for we discovered that the basic notions themselves of velocity, mass, energy, time and space have different significance there.

Space and time are also measured in the microworld by coordinates, yet these coordinates are not used in the ordinary sense but as mathematical tools. They are, if you will, a collection of mathematical "objects" which will spare us the creation of a picture when defining the *position* of an electron in four or more dimensions. Likewise, because the mass of a particle in the microcosmos depends on its velocity, we use the expression *momentum,* which is the product of mass and velocity. And just as time, the fourth variable value, is closely related to spatial coordinates, energy forms a corresponding analogy to *momenta.*

As there is no way, however, to determine accurately a particle's position *and* momentum simultaneously, it makes no sense to talk about the probability of such simultaneous occurrence.

Probability, or the likelihood of the occurrence of an event, had been often applied scientifically since the day Blaise Pascal invented the roulette wheel (often called the "machine of probabilities").

We have also witnessed the acceptance of such statistical law, in place of rigid law, in thermodynamics. Yet, no one departed as far from the classical concepts of natural law than Heisenberg when he replaced probabilities with *uncertainties,* stating that while position *and* momentum can only be given "erroneously" (a harsh word perhaps for something that is 99.999% correct!), the product of these two errors nevertheless *has a definite relation.* The more precisely the position is known, the less precisely the momentum can be known and vice versa. But, asserted Heisenberg, if the coordinate of the position is specified with the uncertainty, Q, and the conjugate momentum with the uncertainty, P, the product of these two uncertainties must always be at least equal to Planck's constant, h, or the elementary quanta. Thus:

$$Q \cdot P = h$$

While the situation outside the nucleus was thus somewhat clarified, the situation inside of the nucleus remained unclear. We remember that almost all the mass of the atom is concentrated in the nucleus and hence space there is rather crowded. While the outside portion of the atom is as empty as the solar system itself, the particles forming the nucleus are jammed tightly together like molecules in an incompressible substance.

First it was supposed that protons, those massive particles with positive electric charges, alone formed the nucleus. But if this were true, the electric charge of the nucleus would be much larger than it actually is. The presence of neutral particles was therefore suspected, and in 1930 J. Chadwick proved the existence of such uncharged particles, since called *neutrons.* We have already mentioned them as an essential component of atomic fission.

But how is it possible that these neutral particles, especially the protons which are positively charged and should therefore repel each other, are held so tightly together? There had to be some powerful attractive force of a non-electric nature which keeps them "glued" together. These so-called *nuclear forces* indeed existed and their behavior was found to be much like that of the adhesive forces holding molecules of different substances together, although these forces are electrical in origin. Nuclear forces are also very strong once contact is established; but their intensity decreases with distance rather swiftly.

This becomes clear when a positively charged particle approaches a nucleus. At first it is repelled as prescribed by Coulomb's law, which says that the force of repulsion between two electrically charged bodies varies in inverse proportion to the square of the distance between them. But if the kinetic energy of the approaching particle is stronger than the force of repulsion, and the particle overcoming this repulsion comes sufficiently close to the nucleus, it is promptly admitted there like a "long-lost relative." Theoretically, it should be allowed to escape under similar circumstances—that is, when its kinetic energy becomes larger than the nuclear forces holding it in the nucleus, just as a prisoner can liberate himself from his shackles if he is strong enough to do so. However, if this were exclusively the case, there would be no natural radioactivity, for particles escaping from the nucleus in the case of radioactive decay have

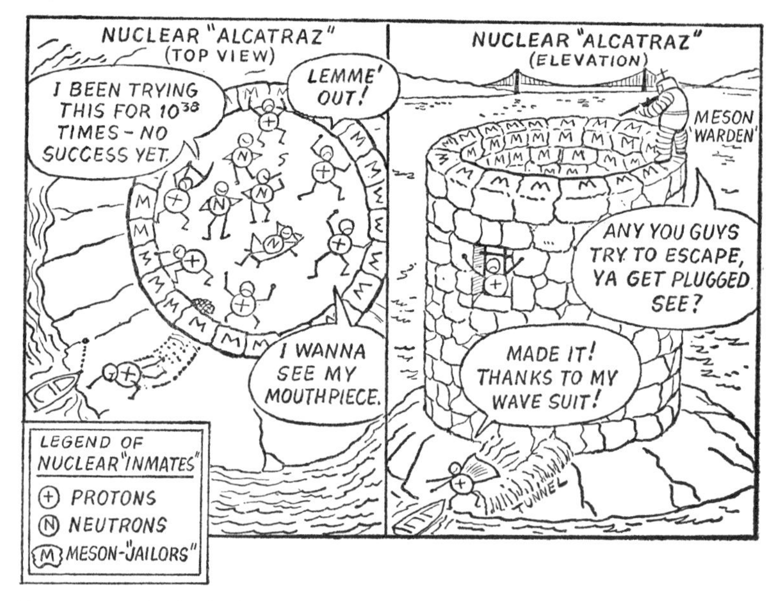

Figure 41. A far-fetched yet graphic representation of the "tunnel effect" within the nucleus of an atom.

lower energy than their nuclear "binding" forces. There must, therefore, be some "secret tunnel" through which the incarcerated particles of the nucleus can escape (Fig. 41). F. Gurney, E. Condon and G. Gamow proved that this was the case.

Gamow considered the particle from the viewpoint of wave mechanics. While the chances of a classical "material" particle escaping from the nucleus are almost zero, a particle accompanied by waves nevertheless has a slim chance of doing so. Yet this chance is still no better than 1 to 10^{38}—a "long shot" indeed. However, as the particle attempts to escape every second at a rate of 10^{21} times,* the probability of its success, though not good, still permits that slight possibility. Indeed, the average "prison term" for alpha particles in the "penitentiary" of a uranium nucleus is about 4½ billion years. This is how long uranium nuclei "live." Without this "tunnel effect," no natural radioactive elements would exist and the artificial splitting of the atom would be an even more complicated business than it already is.

Just what are these mysterious nuclear adhesive forces, these "jailers" of nuclear particles? This question was asked by H. Yukawa, a Japanese physicist, when he suggested that they are themselves atomic particles, later called *mesons*. The existence of mesons was purely hypothetical until Carl Anderson, an American physicist, actually observed them while studying cosmic rays. Anderson wished to solve the riddle of electrons reacting on magnetic fields. While this was logical in the case of protons with considerable mass to be acted upon, it was not explained in the case of electrons with only negligible mass. Anderson found that this was due to another particle also present and as yet undiscovered. This particle had all the properties Yukawa predicted the meson should have, thus confirming its existence.

Yet another particle was also predicted by theories before it was actually confirmed. This was the *neutrino*. It was established that while particles in Alpha rays always possess the same energy when belonging to the same element, Beta particles possess sometimes

* This because its velocity is roughly 10^9 cm/sec, and the size of the "stones" of the prison wall as small as 10^{-12} cm.

more and sometimes less. Therefore, it was postulated that some other particle must account for the difference. The culprit turned out to be the neutrino when Reiner and Cowen, two Americans, finally captured some of them in 1955.

Although the possibility persisted that some of the newly discovered members of the "legitimate" atomic family were actually identical with each other, their number nevertheless grew.

Then there suddenly appeared a whole new tribe of particles out of nowhere! These strange inhabitants of the World of the Most Small claimed to be of *at least the same number* as all the other known particles put together!

This startling theory was presented in 1929 when P. A. M. Dirac, a brilliant British physicist, stated that just as there are electrons which we can measure and locate when they rotate about their nuclei or fly freely off, there are also electron-like particles which we cannot measure because they are located where we imagine *nothing exists but empty space!* At this fantastic notion, the most hardened atomic experts shook their heads in disbelief. Yet when two years later Carl Anderson, the same American who confirmed Yukawa's mesons, also confirmed the existence of Dirac's *anti-electrons,* the search for anti-particles began in earnest.

Today we know that for every particle which exists in nature there is a *twin,* or anti-particle, with opposite properties and charges. Soon after, the uneasy idea of *anti-matter* appeared. We shall consider this in our next chapter.

CHAPTER △ TWENTY-THREE

THE STRANGE WORLD OF ANTI-MATTER

HALF-QUANTA & "SPINNERS"

THE BOHR MAGNETON

RELATIVISTIC WAVE MECHANICS

When Dirac began to study electrons, he had by no means intended to fling open the door on the incredible world of "anti-particles." Rather, his objective had been to eliminate contradictions which existed between the two basic theories of modern physics: the Theory of Relativity and the Quantum Theory. While the quantum theory stated that there are separate, indivisible quanta, the relativity theory was based on non-separate, continuous series of events transforming into each other.

Ever since the creation of quantum mechanics, physicists had been searching for a relativistic form of the quantum aspect which would hold when velocities approaching that of light were involved. When Dirac attacked the problem of hydrogen electrons with this aim in mind, he faced a curious fact. This was the question of *half-quanta*. Even though theory and experience had heretofore confirmed that no lesser quantity of energy than the elementary unit exists, the half of this integer number nevertheless began appearing in both theoretical and empirical studies. Even in the case of a comparatively simple "linear oscillator" with one function, half-quanta had to be used to make the description agree with this experiment.

Experimentation also showed a strange property of electrons—that of their spinning. This was described in 1925 by the Dutch scientists Goudsmit and Uhlenbeck, who stated that when an electron moves about the nucleus and also about its axis it behaves much like the earth moving about its axis and also about the sun. Yet while the earth's motion about its axis is a simple daily rotation, the electron's motion about its so-called "axis of quantization" is actually spiral-like, and is thus a two-phase action. Also, the concept of axis changed, and is different in the microcosmos, inasmuch as it is "quantized" too.

It was Pauli who gave convenient mathematical form to this peculiar spin when, generalizing Schrödinger's wave equation, he introduced his Exclusion Principle. Adding two new functions to the existing one, he stated that no two electrons are the same in every respect. Any electron thus has two choices, but no more than two choices, of spin.

About a year later, Goudsmit and Uhlenbeck found that the two orientations of the spin momentum are equivalent to the two new functions Pauli introduced. Hence, the two phases of the spinning electron correspond to Pauli's two functions.

Now this half-quantum, reasoned Dirac, might very well be the "missing link" between a relativistic-quantum theory if the electron could also be described in terms of a fourth wave function. Schrödinger's equations being basically Newtonian, Dirac therefore had to construct equations with relativistic transformation properties. But the transformation would not work with components of an ordinary four-dimensional coordinate, but like a pair of spinning electrons. These "spinners" proved to be very useful because without them no relativistic electron, postulated by whatever theory, was in accordance with experiment. However, when Dirac included them in his equation, the relativistic electron became a fact confirmed by experiment.

This is how Dirac succeeded in accomplishing the great feat of combining wave mechanics with relativity. Among the consequences was the correct interpretation of the so-called "relativistic fine structure," or the spectral lines which appear between those corresponding to definite energy levels.

Even more important was the deeper understanding of magnetism gained with the introduction of "spinning" electrons. Classical theories of magnetism had already gained a broad new perspective in 1905 when Langevin stated that molecules possess definite "magnetic moments." Such a moment is a combination of distance and force, inasmuch as it is a product of the length of a magnet and the strength of its pole. Magnetic moments of molecules were found to be oriented by force fields. This theory was further developed when Pauli stated that a *natural unit* of magnetic moment also exists: the so-called *Bohr magneton,* which was then identified, by Goudsmit and Uhlenbeck, with the spinning electron. Hence, the fundamental magnetic particle was determined to be "worth" one Bohr magneton.

The Principle of Relativity, even when applied to wave mechanics, implies the appearance of negative quantities, such as the *i*'s which we encountered in a previous chapter. And, regardless of how the forms of these negative quantities change, solutions must also exist for them in this region.

Now, what is a negative particle in reality? It is simply a particle which possesses, instead of positive mass, a negative amount of mass —that is, a mass quantity less than zero! Just as electrons with positive masses have their energy levels, so electrons with negative mass theoretically also have their own levels. Dirac did not hesitate to state that these negative particles must actually exist as predicted by his equations. These "anti-electrons" must, of logical necessity, reasoned Dirac, have the same so-called electronic mass as "normal" electrons only negatively so; that is, while ordinary electrons *do* possess this mass, anti-electrons *do not* possess this mass-amount— *they owe it!*

Such "anti-electrons," Dirac stated, were actually the converse of electrons with equal electric charge; yet, where ordinary electrons were charged negatively, these "extraordinary" electrons held positive charges. Even before their existence was proved, such particles were given the name of "positrons" (see Figure 42). The situation is like this: ordinary electrons with *positive electronic mass* are *negatively* charged electrically. Anti-electrons, positrons with *negative electronic mass,* are *positively* charged.

Now we previously learned that "ordinary" electrons have a tendency to fall from higher energy levels to lower ones. Why then

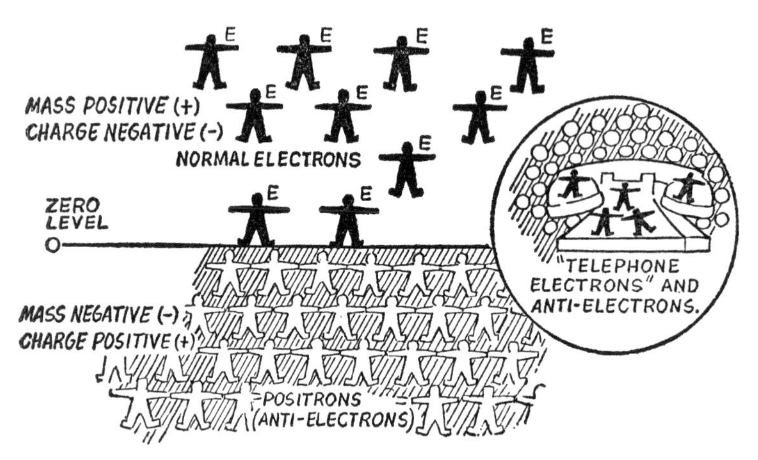

Figure 42. Dirac's strange tribe of anti-electrons with which "empty" space is actually filled. Insert shows comparative scarcity of material electrons to Dirac's "ocean" of surrounding anti-electrons.

do they not fall, after reaching the lowest yet still positive energy level, into the vast sea of negative levels? Obviously, said Dirac, because Pauli's principle holds there too; that is, there is no "place" on the negative energy levels for ordinary electrons. In the immense "ocean" of that which we consider "empty space," negative anti-particles must exist in uniform, close distribution.

Is there no way to make a "hole" among these anti-particles so that an ordinary electron could penetrate this other world from its positive energy level? It is clear that a simple method cannot be employed. We cannot for example "bombard" out anti-particles by hitting them with energy amounts stronger than themselves. No positive energy could "step out" into negative nothingness, as H. G. Wells' hero did when he stepped out of existence into non-existence through a green door. This would be contrary to the law of conservation of energies.

There is, however, a possible, though more complicated, way. This is by hitting a nucleus with *exactly* the necessary amount of energy. By this process an electron *and* a hole in the ranks of the anti-electrons are simultaneously created. This deficiency in the negative level then manifests itself by an appearance in the positive level. In addition to an ordinary electron of positive mass and negative electric charge, its "twin" (a positron having a positive charge) appears in the world of existing particles.

Now this *electron pair,* consisting of an electron and a positron, which Anderson observed while studying cosmic rays, was created naturally. But it may also be created artificially out of an energy amount corresponding to Einstein's formula. Note however that this time energy is not created out of mass, but mass out of energy.

Such an electron pair can also be annihilated. The pair "commits suicide" when its twin components collide with each other. At this point, in effect, H. G. Wells' green door into nothingness is opened. The ordinary electron falls into the "hole" created by the "death" of its other-worldly twin. The masses of both electrons vanish and their equivalent in energy appears instead, as prescribed by Einsteinian law.

Now if anti-electrons exist, anti-protons must exist too! However, as protons possessed considerably more mass, considerably more energy was needed to create a proton-pair consisting of a proton of "our world" having a positive energy state, and an anti-proton from the world of "emptiness" having a negative energy state. This was actually accomplished in 1955.

The rules of creation and annihilation of proton-anti-proton pairs being the same as those valid for electrons, the theoretical possibility of obtaining much larger amounts of energy existed long before artificial collision between ordinary and extraordinary particles was discovered. Remembering the role which the neutron played in atomic fission, we can understand the importance attached in this sense to the anti-neutron, which was finally discovered in 1956.

But how was this discovery possible? The anti-neutron is as electrically neutral as the neutron itself. It was distinguished, however, from the ordinary neutron by its opposite magnetic moment; the magnetic fields around these two particles were of opposite orientation.

Now if an anti-neutron is united with an anti-proton, an antinucleus, or *anti-matter,* is in fact created. This led to the possibility of an energy source far more powerful than any other yet known.

For, when anti-matter encounters matter, both are annihilated and all their mass is capable of being transformed into energy—*not merely* parts of this mass, as in nuclear reactions.

It now seems to be certain that for each particle in our world an anti-particle exists with opposite electric and magnetic properties, yet with equal mass. This mass amount, however, instead of existing in the positive (+) physical world, actually has its being in the negative (−) world of "empty" space where its value is less than zero!

Let us stop a moment and imagine what would be the impressions of our "little folk"—the particles and anti-particles—were they to pay respective visits to each other's world.

A "citizen" of the ordinary electronic world, falling by accident into a chance hole vacated in the "underworld" (the energy-levels lower than zero), would find there a crowded but orderly place. Fortunately he has provided himself with a suit of our special equipment enabling him to see the inhabitants of nothingness; previously, of course, they were not distinguishable to him and were, in fact, simply empty space. Soon he comes to realize that the immense population uniformly distributed in emptiness is much more numerous and better organized than that of his own region, the World of Ordinary Particles. Why? Because there is, in nature, more "space" than matter. Eventually the ordinary electron begins to wonder whether this void full of Below-Zero-Mass-Non-Beings is not the real order of nature—and that the world of the Above-Zero-Mass-Beings from whence he has come is nothing but a lifetime of punishment. Non-existence, to the ordinary citizen of the normal electron world, might seem like Nirvana indeed.

A positron, on the other hand, brought into being and lifted from its negative world, feels equally odd as an intruder among higher-energy-level "ordinary" particles. In the first place, they would seem inaccessible to him, for no particle is supposed to climb to a higher level than its own. In the hierarchy of the microworld, falling from a higher to a lower level is customary; but now the elevated "extraordinary" particle, or positron, is in much the same position as the ordinary electron was in the Negative World. This "positronic citizen" is careful, as he makes his tour of an alien "material" world, to avoid all encounters with his electron "twin"—and indeed with all other "ordinary" particles—lest a fatal collison occur and mutual annihilation take place.

Ordinary particles and their counterparts, the anti-particles, actually hold out bright vistas to science by offering a proof of symmetry in nature—a symmetry of which philosophers and scientists have dreamed since the dawn of human thought. Yet many obstacles still seem to bar the way to this yearned-for harmony. In our last chapter we shall see how the most advanced minds of our century have striven for a final synthesis.

CHAPTER △ TWENTY-FOUR

THE SEARCH FOR FINAL SYNTHESIS

EINSTEIN'S UNIFIED FIELD THEORY
HEISENBERG'S "SHORTEST LENGTH"
"MIRROR IMAGE" & PARITY

Recent physical research has revealed that many of the older concepts describing natural phenomena which once were thought to be separate actually dealt with identical or connected phenomena. Proof of this lies in the links which have subsequently been established between light and invisible radiations, electric and magnetic forces, space and time, energy and matter, weights and masses, and gravitational and inertial effects.

The unification of particle and wave theories, the "atomization" of energy by the introduction of elementary quanta, the wave theory of matter based on *pilot waves,* wave mechanics and their relativistic form—all of these were great steps toward the creation of a basic law, or fundamental equation, which would form the common denominator for all that exists. Yet, there still remained phenomena which, in spite of apparent likeness, could not be reconciled.

We have frequently mentioned the contradictions between laws concerning discrete material particles and those describing their continuous motion. But even in the realm of motion, even among fields, profound differences persisted. While gravitational fields were presented both from physical and geometric viewpoints as the necessary backgrounds of four-dimensional events, the electromagnetic field continued to be considered from a physical viewpoint only. There, distances and the speed of one-dimensional, linear motion only were described.

Likewise, gravitational fields being created about gravitational centers showed a distinct, closed, symmetry, while electromagnetic fields did not possess this characteristic. This meant in technical language that while gravitational fields were characterized by symmetric *tensors,* electromagnetic fields were characterized by anti-symmetric ones.

Moreover, neither of these fields incorporated matter as an integral part of them. One was forced to deal with matter separately. In searching for the final equation, the root of all that exists, Einstein first had to eliminate the difference existing between the two fields. Next, he had to decide whether matter should be treated as a mere concentration of field. One thing was certain: any theory would be untenable in which a part would be described in the language of a continuous field, and the balance in terms of discontinuous matter.

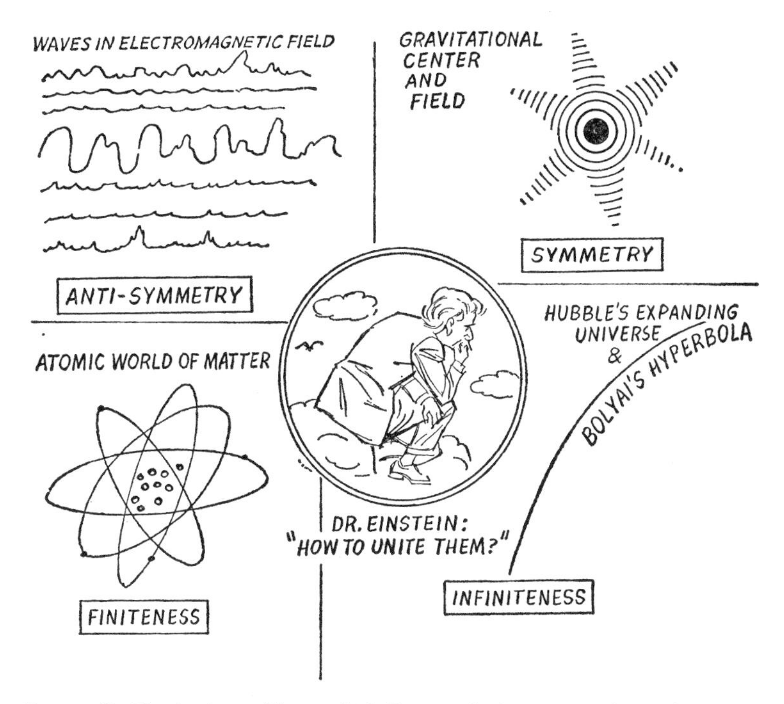

Figure 43. The basic problems which Einstein had to reconcile in the Unified Field Theory.

The field concept, however, had too many advantages to be discarded, and Einstein indeed worked out a *Unified Field Theory* where matter appeared in the form of a finite, strong energy concentration. But, to render the theory universal, it did not suffice to consolidate the concepts of matter and the various fields—that is, merely to unify the gravitational and the electromagnetic field, thus giving a geometry to the latter. Any such theory had to do more; it had to be able to describe equally well the smallest units of matter, such as nuclear particles, and the largest units, such as the galaxies; it had to work as well for weak, gravitational forces as for strong nuclear forces in all existing phenomena. It had to be the most general dynamics possible, incorporating a universal geometry which would include *Bolyaian, Riemannian, Euclidian* and indeed all possible geometries.

Einstein struggled with this gigantic task for more than thirty years (Fig. 43). His passionate desire was to present one classical, rigid law as the all-embracing key to the universe. He believed utterly in causes and their inevitable effects; moreover, he was convinced that all rules of statistical probability which worked well inside the atom were temporary and would be finally replaced by positive natural laws. "I believe," Einstein once said, "in an existing world and that it is somehow possible to learn its order. I cannot accept the fact that God simply throws dice."

Indeed, Einstein had good reason to believe that he would succeed in making a final order among the scientific legacies willed to him and his contemporaries. Already worked out, for example, were equations for gravitation, electricity and magnetism—all of which contained certain important similarities—namely, all three of them depended on a tested constant. Also, it was known that forces were inversely proportional to the square of distance. The spacetime position of mass particles in the gravitational field differed only slightly from that of their neighbors, just as wave motion was described by adequate differential equations in electromagnetic fields. The roles played in the gravitational field by *masses* were described in terms of *charges* and *strengths* of magnetic poles. Yet, while in the case of magnetism and electricity electromagnetic forces were attractive and repulsive ones, gravitational force was considered to be only attractive—unless the concept of gravitational repulsion was introduced.

Hence, any new all-inclusive theory had to encompass all of these previous ones if it were to be crowned with success. Just as Newton's gravitational laws were a good first approximation of the more general Einsteinian gravitational law, and just as special relativity was a special case of the general theory, the Unified Field Theory proposed to include all functions of these earlier theories—and these were sixteen in number! Six of them covered the electromagnetic field as expressed in *anti-symmetric* tensor equations, and ten of them the gravitational field expressed by *symmetric* tensor equations.

Matter was to be deduced from these field equations, and every physical concept was to have its geometrical counterpart in the complete unified field. The Unified Field Theory proposed to present the geometry of our entire cosmos by means of physics.

But did it? Does the Unified Field Theory really satisfactorily include everything that exists?

Alas, it now appears that Einstein was to be deprived of achieving this final goal of complete synthesis. Even he could not provide that last great bond uniting all the threads of universal existence. The Unified Field Theory proved to be too rigidly harmonious to include all the wild titanic forces rushing through outer space, too unflexible in its beauty to capture the unobservable uncertainties operating inside the World of the Most Small.

And yet, another attempt to find at least a bridge between the theories of relativity and quanta was made by Werner Heisenberg, author of the Uncertainty Principle.

Heisenberg made this public when he delivered a speech in April of 1958 on the occasion of Max Planck's 100th birthday. He, Pauli and their co-workers in Göttingen found that the unification of these two theories could only be achieved when, in addition to c, light's constant velocity, and Planck's constant, h, the element of action (cornerstones respectively of the theories of relativity and quanta), a *third* natural constant is introduced. This third constant represents the *shortest length* within which interactions of nuclear particles take place. This value is a bit smaller than the diameter of a typical nucleus, or about 10^{-13}cm.

In addition to the well-known physical divergences between the theories of relativity and quantum, Heisenberg emphasized the inherent philosophical contradictions. The Theory of Relativity marks sharp limits between past, present, and future. The past is conceived as all of that upon which we may have exact data; the future as all of that upon which we may principally have influence. Between them stands the infinitely short present moment. This concept of present, however, became finite when Einstein proved that it has a duration which increases with distance. As no data from an observed event can reach us quicker than with the velocity of light, the remoter an event is, the more distinct the distance which separates the past and future becomes.

The Uncertainty Principle however taught us that such rigid distinction is impossible in the domain of the smallest quanta. When Dirac succeeded in building a bridge between *relativistic dynamics* and *wave mechanics* he tried to enlarge that structure by applying his method explicitly to the field theory of quanta. He suggested that the negative *i* quantities should be used to give a kind of indefinite metric "geometry" to space. But this would involve negative probabilities, that is, the probability of the happening of an event would be negative, which is physically an absurd concept.

This could not be so, maintained Heisenberg, if the negative quantities would only appear when we are inquiring after conditions within the space dimension of the shortest length, that is, 10^{-13}cm. Anything greater than this value would be positive.

We have seen that events within the smallest spacetime unit cannot be observed directly. But might not probabilities there be studied mathematically?

Heisenberg believes that he has worked out the first model to this very purpose. The basis for it is a simple equation in which the electromagnetic field may appear as a consequence of fields surrounding matter. Here matter is manifested in particles which show properties similar to those observed experimentally.

The proposed equation is (and Heisenberg points out that it is a

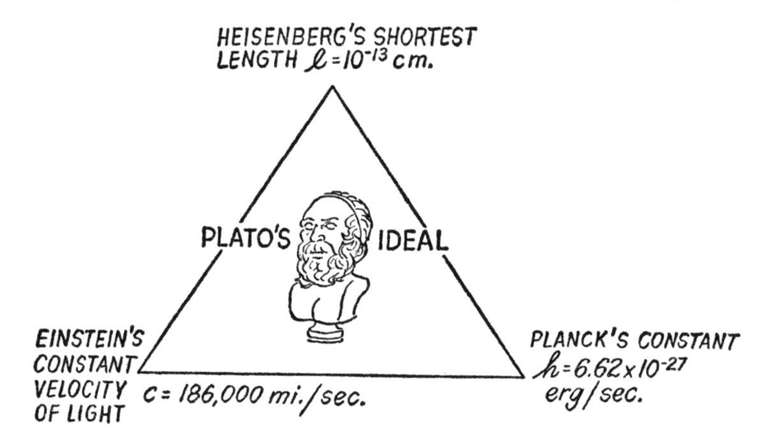

Figure 44. How the three constants *c*, *h*, and *l* resemble the triangular nature of Plato's Ideal System of Knowledge.

proposition only) remarkable in its simplicity. In it, besides matter, the linear transformation and the three constants form a symmetry which is, in its threefold nature, singularly like Plato's ideal (Fig. 44). Yet, while 2000 years ago the Greek philosopher designated the *triangle* as the basic image after which all existing elements were formed, the modern physicist must present the fundamental mathematical idea, *dependent upon physical constants,* which he believes governs matter and motion.

The first two of these (Planck's h and Einstein's c) have been proven again and again by experiment. But what is the proof of the third?

Measurement of this shortest length can only be done by the statistical methods which seem, for the time being at least, to be the only way of studying such tiny values. We must never forget, however, that these statistics are, in a way, contrary to those used in ordinary measurements. If we wish to know, for example, the popularity of a certain washday product, we take a poll of, say, 10,000 women. If 8,000 of them report that they use it, we may assert that the majority prefers the product. In the atomic world, however, we can only establish a chain of events *in reverse order.* This would be the same as saying that by the very fact of establishing that the majority of women had chosen the product, we would *ipso facto* be able to predict that 8,000 out of 10,000 *must have* done so. When we know by experimentation, for instance, which particles transform into which other particles, we can draw definite conclusions as to their choice.

This law of selection generally shows a symmetry. What is physical symmetry? We say that a physical system has a definite symmetry or *parity* when it is identical with its *mirror image.* We are all acquainted, for example, with the notion that for every action there also exists its mirror action; hence, there is no real difference between a left-hand process and a right-hand one.

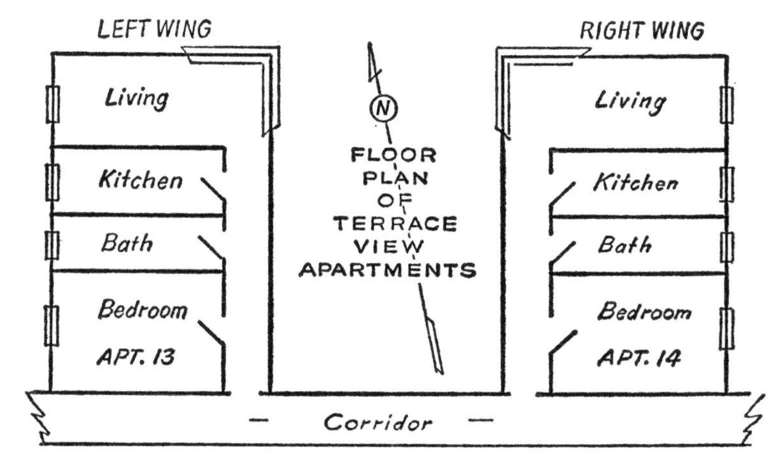

Figure 45. A simple example of *parity*. Apartment 13 in the left wing is a "mirror image" of Apartment 14 in the right wing.

To illustrate this, suppose we apply at the renting office of an apartment house. The agent in charge tells us that he is not able to show us the exact apartment we wish to rent because it is still occupied. He can, however, show us exactly the same apartment in the opposite wing (Fig. 45). In other words, we will be able to inspect the left-hand version of the right-hand apartment we shall eventually occupy. What we are seeing, in effect, is a mirror image, or a preview-in-reverse, of our future home.

Such definite *parity* also reigns in the nucleus of an atom. That is, it generally emits as many particles in one direction as it does in the other. In 1957, however, two Chinese physicists, C. Y. Yang and T. D. Lee, asserted that in certain cases of radioactive decay this parity is not always conserved.

This was experimentally proven by yet another Chinese physicist, Madame Wu. By cooling an atomic system sufficiently to make the axes of all nuclei align in the same direction, she was able to measure accurately the direction of emitted electrons. Madame Wu found that more electrons were emitted in one direction than the other!

The reason for this was not because the electrons arbitrarily "preferred" one direction to another, but because they were accompanied by *neutrinos*. And, as Pauli also noticed earlier, neutrinos, contrary to all other particles, do not possess a definite parity, but follow a right-hand spiral motion. Apparently no left-hand spiraling neutrinos exist!

Therefore, wouldn't neutrinos, having no mirror images, be *exceptions* to the law of parity? Not if we suggest the idea of an *anti-*

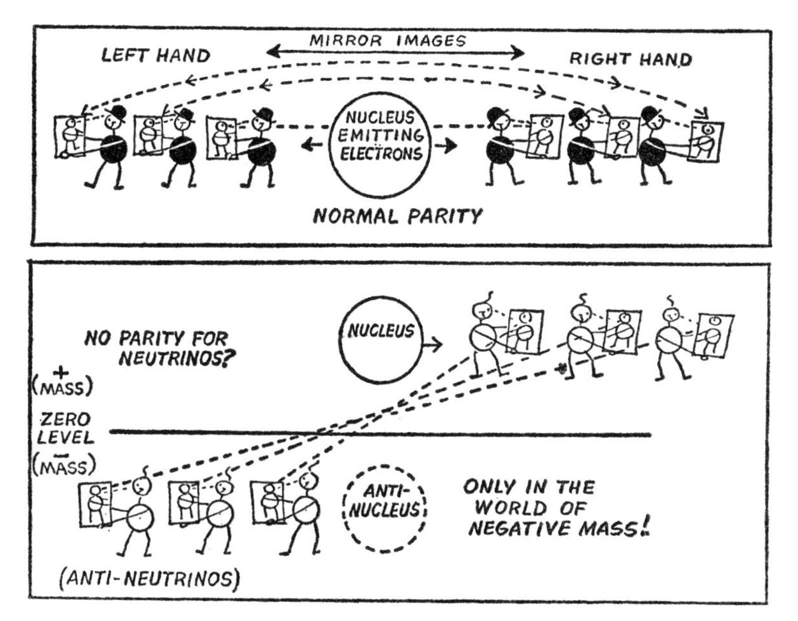

Figure 46. How the peculiar *parity* of neutrinos is preserved by anti-electrons.

neutrino emitted by an *anti-nucleus* together with the *anti-electrons,* or *positrons,* with which we are already familiar (Fig. 46). Such an anti-neutrino would follow just the opposite direction and its orientation in the electromagnetic field would be that of a left-hand spiral.

Hence, parity of the neutrino would be conserved in its respect to the anti-neutrino. Now anti-particles, as we know, possess opposite electrical charges from those of their corresponding "normal" particles. Thus, by simply changing the sign of the electric charges, we obviate the necessity of demanding opposite action in space to achieve parity.

This apparently simple consequence of Lee and Yang's discovery, further developed by the Soviet physicist L. Landau, is an unexpected contribution to the linking-up of charge and space—two concepts always considered as separate. It may also be an important step toward the final goal: harmony in nature.

Out of both the grand unity of which Einstein dreamed and the symmetry suggested by Heisenberg, is there any hope of forging the One Common Bond uniting all physical phenomena? Whatever answer we could give here would certainly be altered by future developments.

Is it not more logical to assume that each new law of nature, regardless of how final it may appear, is but another step forward towards a synthesis in which contradictory theses may eventually become united? And the new synthesis itself might be challenged by yet a newer theory—to be united still later in an even more complete synthesis.

We have learned much about nature on our Guided Tour. We now know something about energy and matter, and a great deal about motion. We have also learned something about the mathematical order which all these phenomena seem to obey. And yet, we are still not certain whether all our knowledge might not be different were we, the observers, different, too.

We have, in addition, learned the inexorable verdict of the Second Law of Thermodynamics, which condemns our universe to a timeless, heatless death. We have scrutinized the microcosmos to obtain more favorable solutions, yet the only consolation we found there was probability and uncertainty. And yet—were not all mortal things once born? If our world, as we know it, is doomed to end, did it not also have a beginning? And, once created, might it not be created again?

Alas, such final answers cannot be given by present-day physics. Rather, it is the goal of physics to ask questions and to be satisfied with temporary answers. During our Guided Tour we have attempted to present some of them . . . sometimes, it is true, by reinforcing our special equipment with a bit of imagination. Gradually, however, we saw that even these resources were not of much use to us in the realms of the Most Great and the Most Small.

Yet, the development of physics does not stop simply because seemingly insurmountable obstacles lie ahead. We trust that it never shall cease. It is for this reason that the history of physics, like our humble book, remains an unfinished story.

APPENDIX OF SIGNIFICANT EQUATIONS

(1) $$x^* = \frac{x - vt}{\sqrt{1 - v^2/c^2}}$$

(2) $$t^* = \frac{t - \frac{v}{c^2}x}{\sqrt{1 - v^2/c^2}}$$

(A simplified presentation of the Lorentz Transformation, the basis of the Theory of Special Relativity, where:

x^* = "length axis" of coordinate No II

x = "length axis" of coordinate No I

t^* = "time axis" of coordinate No II

t = "time axis" of coordinate No I

v = velocity

c^2 = the square of the velocity of light in cm/seconds)

(3) $$E = mc^2, \qquad \text{and} \qquad m = \frac{E}{c^2}$$

(Einstein's Law of the Equivalence of Mass and Energy where:

E = energy (in ergs)

m = mass (in grams)

c^2 = the square of the velocity of light in cm/seconds)

(4) $$E = hv$$

(Energy amount of a light quantum where:

E = energy of the light quantum

h = Planck's Quantum Constant or $6.624 \cdot 10^{-27}$ erg/sec.

v = frequency of the radiation, or vibrations/sec.)

(5) $$\lambda = \frac{h}{mv}$$

(De Broglie's wave length where:

λ (lambda) = wave length

h = Planck's Constant

m = mass
v = velocity } momentum)

(6) $$\Delta x \cdot \Delta v = \frac{h}{m}$$

(Heisenberg's Uncertainty Relation, where:

Δx = the value of the coordinate (between x and $\pm\Delta x$)

Δv = the value of the velocity (between v and $\pm\Delta v$)

m = mass

h = Planck's Constant.)

GLOSSARY

ACCELERATION—rate of change of velocity.

ADHESION—force which holds unlike molecules together.

ALPHA—(a) particle: the nucleus of a helium atom which is positively charged; (b) rays: stream of fast-moving alpha particles.

AMPLITUDE—extent of vibratory motion measured from the mean position to the maximum departure.

ANGULAR DISTANCE—distance between two points measured in degrees of an angle subtended by them at point of observation.

ANGULAR VELOCITY—rate of change of a point in motion about an axis.

ANNIHILATION RADIATION—energy emission caused by colliding electrons and positrons, which annihilate each other.

ANTI-PARTICLES—(a) anti-electron: a positron; (b) anti-matter: anti-nucleus consisting of anti-protons and anti-neutrons; (c) anti-neutron: neutron possessing a magnetic moment opposite to the neutron; (d) anti-proton: a negatively charged proton.

APERTURE—opening in optical instruments which admits radiation.

ATOM—the smallest part of an element able to take part in chemical reactions. It consists essentially of a positively charged nucleus and negatively charged electrons.

ATOMIC NUMBER—a number equal to the number of protons in the nucleus, and determining the element to which the atom belongs.

AXIS—an ideal line about which a system rotates or about which a geometric figure is symmetrical.

BETA—(a) particle: fast-moving electron emitted by radioactive substance; (b) rays: stream of high-speed electrons emitted by such radioactive decay.

BLACK BODY—an ideal light absorber and emitter of radiations of all frequencies.

BROWNIAN MOTION—random movement of microscopic particles of a solid suspended in a fluid or gaseous substance.

CENTRIFUGAL FORCE—outward force which compels a rotating body to recede from its pivotal point; equal yet opposite in sign from centripetal force (q.v.).

CENTRIPETAL FORCE—force which impels a rotating body toward its pivotal point, thus preventing it from flying off in a straight line; equal yet opposite in sign from centrifugal force (q.v.).

COEFFICIENT—a factor constant for the system it measures.

COHESION—attraction exerted between like molecules.

CONSERVATION OF MASS AND ENERGY—principle that the total amount of energy and mass, multiplied by c^2, is constant for any system.

CONTINUUM—a continuous series of parts passing into one another.

COORDINATE—(a) one of the magnitudes which determine positions on planes, and in three or more dimensional spaces; (b) Cartesian coordinate system: a system with rectilinear axes.

COSMIC RAYS—radiation from outer space consisting principally of high-energy atomic nuclei.

DECAY (Radioactive)—spontaneous emission of rays by radioactive nuclei.

DENSITY—mass per unit volume of a substance.

DEUTERIUM—hydrogen isotope, also known as "heavy hydrogen."

DIFFRACTION OF LIGHT—special case of interference occurring near the edges of a light beam passing through an aperture; i.e., the spreading of light as it bends slightly about the aperture.

DIFFUSION OF LIGHT—scattering of light passing through an aperture; or its reflection by a rough reflecting surface.

DISPERSION OF LIGHT—splitting of a beam of white light into various colors of the spectrum as it passes into another medium, as from air to glass.

DYNAMICS—branch of physics describing forces which produce changes in motion.

ELECTROLYSIS—chemical decomposition produced by electrical current.

ELECTRON—generally, a negatively charged particle revolving about the nucleus of an atom; the elementary unit of electrical charge.

ELECTRON "SPIN"—spiral-like two-phase action of an electron about its axis of quantization.

ENERGY—the capacity to perform work. Potential, kinetic, chemical, electrical, atomic, thermal and radiant energies are interconvertible.

ENTROPY—the measure of unavailability of heat due to the irreversible course of thermal energy from hot to cold.

EQUILIBRIUM—state of balance; also the state in which neither changes in linear nor angular velocity can occur.

EXCLUSION PRINCIPLE—the principle that no two electrons of an atomic system can be exactly equivalent; also, that no more than two electrons can occupy one quantum orbit of an atom.

FIELD—area or region traversed by lines of force.

FISSION (Nuclear)—splitting of heavy-nucleus atoms to produce atomic energy.

FORCE—work done per unit of distance, also cause of acceleration.

FREQUENCY—number of oscillations per second of a wave motion.

GAMMA RAYS—radiation of very short electomagnetic wavelengths by radioactive substances.

GEODESICS—shortest distance between two points on a sphere.

GRAPH—diagram showing relationships between variables.

GRAVITATION—the force of attraction between two material bodies.

HEAT—kinetic energy associated with molecules in random motion.

HEAVY WATER—water in which ordinary hydrogen is substituted by heavy hydrogen (deuterium).

HYDROGEN BOMB—thermonuclear bomb whose energy is caused mainly by the fusion of hydrogen isotopes, induced by high temperatures.

HYPERBOLA—an open curve, having only one focus, formed by a section of a right circular cone when the cutting side makes a greater angle with the base than the cone's side makes.

i—symbol for elemental imaginary number, $\sqrt{-1}$. Imaginary numbers have negative squares.

INERTIA—natural tendency of a body to preserve its state of rest or uniform motion.

INFINITY—without end; something which is greater than any assignable quantity.

INTERFERENCE OF LIGHT—phenomenon occurring when two beams of light meet. If two beams of light meet so that wave *crests* of one coincide with the crests of the second, increased light results; however, when crests coincide with *troughs,* light is cancelled out.

INTERMOLECULAR FORCES—forces holding molecules together.

ISOTOPE—atoms of the same chemical element, but differing in atomic weight.

KINETIC ENERGY—the energy a body possesses by the fact of its motion.

LIGHT—generally, that part of the electromagnetic spectrum which produces visible radiation.

LIGHT YEAR—the distance traveled by light in one year, or about 6,000,000,000,000 miles.

MACROCOSM—generally, the world of large-scale objects, as distinguished from very small objects such as atomic particles.

MACROSTATE—the action, considered from the viewpoint of many quantities, in the physical world.

MAGNETIC MOMENT—the product of the distance between the two poles of a magnet and the strength of either pole.

MASS—the quantity of matter in a body and its attitude toward accelerating forces. Acceleration being proportional to the force, the mass is the constant of proportionality of the body.

MATERIAL POINT—the least portion of any material particle.

MECHANICS—branch of physics dealing with the effect of forces on bodies; Newtonian mechanics provides accurate data for ordinary velocity motions.

MESON—subatomic particle discovered in cosmic rays with mass intermediary between an electron and a proton.

MICROCOSM—generally, the submicroscopic atomic world, as distinguished from large-scale objects.

MICROSTATE—the action, considered from the viewpoint of one individual quantity, of the atomic world.

MIRROR IMAGE—image of a physical system as seen in a mirror.

MOLECULES—atoms held together by chemical means; the smallest particles of any substance still possessing the property of that substance.

MOMENTUM—the product of mass times velocity.

NEUTRINO—an uncharged weightless particle.

NEUTRON—a heavy, uncharged particle forming part of the nucleus of an atom.

NOBLE GASES—gases which do not combine chemically with any element.

NUCLEAR FORCES—forces acting inside the nucleus of an atom.

NUCLEAR REACTION—disintegration of the atomic nucleus, occurring either naturally or produced artificially.

NUCLEUS—the core of the atom.

OPTICS—branch of physics dealing with light and its phenomena.

OSCILLATOR—anything emitting waves; that which oscillates.

PARABOLA—a conic section, formed by the intersection of the cone by a plane parallel to its side.

PARITY—the definite symmetry of a physical system; its identity with its mirror-image.

PERIODIC SYSTEM—the chemical elements arranged in order of their regularly recurring physical and chemical properties.

PHOTOELECTRIC EFFECT—emission of electrons by a substance when acted upon by radiation of a suitable frequency.

PHOTON—elementary *quantum* of radiant energy.

pi (or π)—the ratio of the circumference of a circle to its diameter; good to four decimal places, this value is 3.1415.

PLANCK'S CONSTANT—*h*, the quantum "element of action," or 6.624×10^{-27} ergs, where "erg" is the unit of energy.

POLARIZATION OF LIGHT—the reduction of ordinary light to waves whose oscillations are all in the same plane.

POSITRON—a positively charged electron discovered in cosmic rays.

PROTON—a positively charged constituent of the atomic nucleus, with a mass approximately 1,840 times greater than that of an electron.

QUANTUM—an elemental amount of energy associated with electromagnetic waves of a given frequency.

QUANTUM THEORY—the theory, advanced by Planck, that radiant energy is emitted or absorbed in tiny but definite amounts called *quanta.*

QUANTUM MECHANICS—a development of the Quantum Theory in which particles are associated with waves. Such particles have characteristics which are in accord with wave behavior and also the theory of definite quanta.

RADIOACTIVITY—the spontaneous distintegration of unstable atomic nuclei. Artificial radioactivity is the man-made accomplishment of this process.

RELATIVITY—the theory, as advanced by Einstein, that if two systems are in relative motion with uniform straight-line velocity, there is no way for observers in either system to determine this motion in an absolute way. Also, that the velocity of light in any system is constant. Special Relativity covers cases of pure motion proceeding at constant linear velocity through empty space; it also defines the mass of a body in motion as greater than its mass at rest, and the interconvertibility of mass and energy. General Relativity deals with cases of non-uniform motion and introduces a new theory of gravitation.

REFRACTION OF LIGHT—the bending of a light ray, or other radiation, as it passes from one medium to another.

SPECTRUM—generally, the image formed by radiant energy dispersed and brought to a focus so that waves are arranged in order of their lengths.

SPEED—magnitude of motion only, as opposed to velocity (q.v.).

SUPERSPACE—space of more than three dimensions, also called *hyperspace.*

TENSOR—a generalized concept of a directed magnitude described by more than three components.

THERMODYNAMICS—branch of physics dealing with laws governing heat processes: FIRST LAW: heat and mechanical work are mutually convertible; SECOND LAW: heat cannot be transferred by any self-sustaining process from a cooler to a hotter system.

THERMONUCLEAR REACTION—fusion caused by high temperature; the liberation of nuclear energy induced by high temperature.

TRANSVERSE WAVE—a wave whose vibrations are at right angles to the direction of its propagation.

UNCERTAINTY PRINCIPLE—the impossibility of determining both position and momentum of an atomic particle simultaneously and perfectly.

VALENCY—the combining capacity of the atoms of an element.

VARIABLE—non-constant quantity which may assume different or even distinct values.

VELOCITY—the rate of motion in a given direction measured by length *per* time.

VOLUME—amount of space occupied by a body.

WAVELENGTH—the distance between corresponding points in two successive waves.

WAVE MECHANICS—the dynamics of particles and waves (see QUANTUM MECHANICS).

WORK—the accomplishment of a force through a given distance; work equals the force times the distance through which it acts.

INDEX